WRITING

FOR AGES 5–7

Gillian Howell

Andrew Brodie ✓

First published 2009 by A&C Black Publishers Limited
36 Soho Square, London W1D 3QY
www.acblack.com

ISBN 978-1-4081-2482-6

Series Editor Julia Stanton
Design © Anita Ruddell 2009
Cover photographs © Shutterstock
Illustrations © Bridget Mackeith

Photo credits: p. 22 IStock/Steve Debenport/Vikram Raghuvanshi/Randy Plett; RS 41 Istock/Robyn Mackenzie/Stanislav Pobytov/Sergey Kolodkin; .
RS 8 Shutterstock/Thumb/Claudio Zaccherini; RS 9 Shutterstock/Matt Ragen/Mikhail Nekrasov; RS 11 Shutterstock/Andreas Doppelmayr/Arvind
Balaraman/Leah-Anne Thompson/Supri Suharjoto/Blacqbook/Lucian Coman; RS 30 Shutterstock/Hagit Berkovich/Arvind Balaraman;
RS 36 Shutterstock/Leah-Anne Thompson; RS 38 Shutterstock/ Ivonne Wierink/Dole/Rob Wilson/Charlie Hutton/Rick's Photography/
MalibuBooks; RS 53 Shutterstock/ Thomas Sztanek; RS 54 Shutterstock/ Eric Gevaert/Gerrit de Vries

Printed in Great Britain by Martins the Printers, Berwick-Upon-Tweed

This book is produced using paper that is made from wood grown in
managed, sustainable forests. It is natural, renewable and recyclable.
The logging and manufacturing processes conform to the environmental
regulations of the country of origin.

**To see our full range of titles
visit www.acblack.com**

Contents

Introduction

Brilliant Ideas to Get Boys Writing aims to provide positive strategies and practical resources for boys, in particular, as they develop their writing skills in the classroom. All children become better writers by engaging in the process of writing often, although research in the last ten years has shown that boys face particular difficulties and therefore require targeted help to attain their potential. As in all learning, teachers are key to this process and many of the strategies to improve writing are the same for boys and girls, such as creating an inviting and creative environment. However, there are other strategies, such as an emphasis on 'active learning' and 'talk' which are more important to the acquisition of skills by boys.

The strategies which help boys become enthusiastic and independent authors, writing for different purposes and audiences are:

★ Creating an inviting environment
★ Providing good literature and text models
★ Planning for and understanding the writing process
★ Giving real and relevant reasons for (boys) writing
★ Creating active learning strategies, including talk and drama
★ The inclusion of visual media
★ The use of ICT
★ Planning meaningful cross-curricular activities
★ Using assessment and reflection

These strategies underpin all the activities and resources in this book. The activities are easy to follow and the instruction text has been kept to a minimum to make them less daunting for boys. All the activity and resource sheets can be used on their own or alongside other literacy schemes that are already established in your school. Throughout the book you will find lots of references to good literacy practices, such as shared reading and writing, adult scribing, demonstration, supported composition, in addition to the specific strategies to develop writing independence. Boys will develop and gain greater success and confidence in an atmosphere of support and encouragement. Praise from a caring adult can be the best reward for their efforts. The activities in this book will provide many opportunities for them to enjoy success and build confidence which, in turn, will develop a positive attitude towards writing and a resulting increase in self-esteem.

The writing process

The writing process is made up of specific steps. These are the steps used by all writers although, depending on the writing purpose and audience, some of them may be short-circuited. The units in Brilliant Ideas to Get Boys Writing develop these steps, giving emphasis to different features as the units progress.

The steps are:
★ **Pre-writing**
   Features talk and active learning strategies to gather thoughts and ideas, individually or in groups. Stage to define the purpose of the writing and the audience for the finished text.

★ **Making notes and drafting**
   Includes making notes of ideas and thoughts, discussing them and altering and adding to them. Stage to make first attempt at writing task and checking purpose and text type.

★ **Revising and polishing**
   The writer or writers improve their text, individually or in collaboration with others – altering and adding language features and improving vocabulary and text organisation.

★ **Editing and proofreading**
   Writers can check the language mechanics of their own text or have others do it for them.

★ **Reading and publishing**
   Sharing of text with audience, through a variety of media.

Brilliant strategies

Create an inviting environment
★ Have high expectations of boys
★ Engage and motivate reluctant boys
★ Promote confidence and creativity
★ Reflect boys' interests

Provide good literature and text models
★ Have available a varied mix of books which appeal to boys and reflect personal interests
★ Provide emotionally powerful texts and varied text types, including visual texts
★ Include literature with appropriate role models
★ Include popular and 'out of school' cultural models

Plan for and understanding the writing process
★ Plan brisk and structured lessons with clearly stated objectives
★ Include varied activities, building an understanding of the process
★ Demonstrate modelling of texts
★ Provide opportunities for paired and collaborative tasks
★ Use plenty of writing frames to provide structure, modify to suit tasks

Give real and relevant reasons for (boys) writing
★ Create a writing habit, a classroom focus, across subjects
★ Give choices in topic settings, particularly narrative
★ Use relevant topics and interests – boys respond well to real-world themes
★ Include an element of competition and allow boys to challenge themselves

Plan meaningful cross-curricular activities
★ Plan to introduce content and tasks from other subjects
★ Identify and use genres and text types associated with particular subjects
★ Plan writing tasks in specific subject areas to give boys a sense of real-world purpose

Create active learning strategies
★ Boys show a preference for active learning – provide opportunities throughout lessons
★ Use talk often – it helps boys in the formulation and articulation of ideas
★ Explicitly discuss models of writing and explore how writer's write
★ Use dramatic strategies, help develop understanding and expression

Include visual media
★ Boys respond to opportunities to work with visual media – cartoons, television, video etc.
★ Visual media as a starting point can help boys develop literacy and move to written text types
★ Use visual 'graphic organisers' to help structure text planning
★ Use visual texts to convey meaning and support written text types

Make use of ICT
★ Use multi-media text to stimulate discussion and ideas
★ ICT supports active and interactive task development and outcomes
★ Use ICT at all stages of the writing process
★ Use presentation software to increase boys' confidence

Use assessment and reflection
★ Set clear targets and link assessment to them
★ Give regular feedback, including individual progress
★ Use self-assessment and partner/peer review to encourage discussion of learning
★ Challenge boys to extend their writing

Worth reading
★ *Me Read? No Way!* A practical guide to improving boys' literacy skills – Ontario Education
★ *Improving boys' writing through visual literacy and drama* – Developed by Lancashire Literacy Team
★ *Literature search on improving boys' writing* – Caroline Daly, OFSTEAD

Using this book

For teachers:

Purpose, structure, language and visual features of text type.

Examples of 'forms' within the text type, or exemplars of the text type.

Suggestions for cross-curricular opportunities.

narrative fiction

Purpose	to interest and entertain
Structure	events in sequential order; beginning (introducing characters and setting), middle (events and problems) and ending (resolution)
Language features	usually past tense verbs; story book language 'Once there was...'; descriptive language and dialogue; first or third person pronouns
Visual features	often has illustrations, which can support the reader
Examples	*The Tiger who came to Tea*, by Judith Kerr; *Not Now Bernard*, by David McKee; *Horrid Henry* stories by Francesca Simon

Cross-curricular suggestions

Art and design
★ Children represent characters and settings using art and design skills.

Geography
★ Children can explore settings, both imaginary and 'realistic' and use mapping skills to describe them to others.

PSHE
★ Children can discuss events and issues raised in narratives with reference to their own lives.

9

Notes for each activity, with emphasis on strategies to support boys' engagement and learning.

Challenges, opportunities, further activities to extend the unit.

Activity and talk-based ideas, which support boys learning, for getting started.

Links to numerous Resource Sheets and General Reference support materials available on the CD.

Suggestions for reflection and feedback opportunities.

teacher's notes

Use the **Challenge Cards** (Resource Sheet 5) to extend the unit.

Activity Sheet 1
Read the model text on Resource Sheet 1 with the children. Display the questions for reflection on Resource Sheet 2 and ask children to discuss them in small groups. Then display the model again and discuss the structure of the text with the class. Point out the sequence of beginning, middle and ending and identify the characters. Together, highlight the words that show the passing of time, dialogue and descriptive words. Provide the children with the activity sheet. Ask them to work with a partner and draw or write answers to the 'what happened?' questions.

Activity Sheet 2
Discuss stories being read by the class and orally explore 'what happened?' by asking the children to describe what happens in the beginning, middle and ending. Choose a story the children are familiar with and which has a clear structure. Ask them to use the activity sheet to draw or write what happened in each part of the story.

Activity Sheet 3
Talk with the children about the settings of the model text: the flat, the park and Grandad's house. Ask them to think about what Danny might have seen in these places. Display Resource Sheet 3 or give it to children in groups, and use the prompts to describe one of the settings. If time permits give groups time to 'create' or draw each of the settings and display them. Similarly, discuss the settings of stories that are currently being read. What can characters see, hear, smell and feel there? What time of day is it? What is the weather like? Can characters hear anything there? Encourage the children to expand their responses and generate lots of describing words by asking questions. Ask the children to draw and write about a setting from one of their favourite stories using the activity sheet.

Activity Sheet 4
Talk with the children about the characters in the model text: Danny, Dad, Mum and Grandad. Discuss what they think the characters are like, for example: Danny, six years old, an only child perhaps, likes animals; Mum, dislikes mini-beasts; Grandad is kind. Discuss what characters are like in stories that are currently being read and how some stories tell you a lot about the characters and others let you guess what they are like. Ask the children to choose a character they like from one of the stories, close their eyes and picture the character in their mind's eye. Tell them to add details about the character to the activity sheet.

Activity Sheet 5
Display and discuss General Reference sheet 'Planning a story'. Ask the children to write their own version of the story 'A Dog for Danny'. Discuss how they could change the main character, Danny, for a character of their own. Compare the settings the children described in activity 3. Discuss how they could change the setting. Talk about the plot. What could the new character want in their new setting and why can't they get it? How do they overcome the problem? Ask the children to draw and write their new version of the story using the activity sheet to plan it first.

REFLECTION & FEEDBACK suggestions

Discuss how stories tell us 'what happened'. Ask the children to suggest why it is important to have a beginning, middle and ending in stories. Ask them to say which sort of characters they like to write about and why. Similarly, which settings they enjoy describing and why.

getting started

Display
Create a display of stories that appeal to boys. Enlist boys from the class to choose which books should be included in the display.

Role-play
Give the children a simple scenario, for example, going shopping. Arrange them in pairs and give them two character cards from Resource Sheet 4. Ask them to role-play going shopping, as the characters on the cards.

Tell me why?
Read a simple story to the children. At strategic points stop the story and ask the children to tell you why something happened or why someone did or said something.

Act and tell
Describe an action to begin a story in the first person and simultaneously act it out, for example, as you act out sweeping the floor, say 'I was sweeping the floor one day when I saw a...' Stop and ask the children to suggest what it was. Choose one of the children to continue the story, act it out and stop at the last word of the sentence. Continue so all the children are included.

Action story circle
Arrange the children into a circle. Using a simple story, rhyme or poem they are all familiar with, ask them to perform another action while they tell the story, for example, standing on one leg, hopping, or patting the top of their head. As soon as a child stops the action or runs out of words, the next child continues the story.

11

For pupils:

Activity Sheets
Up to nine Activity Sheets for each text type unit.

Learning Objective for each activity.

Emphasis on a range of strategies, exploring texts and building appropriate text type structure.

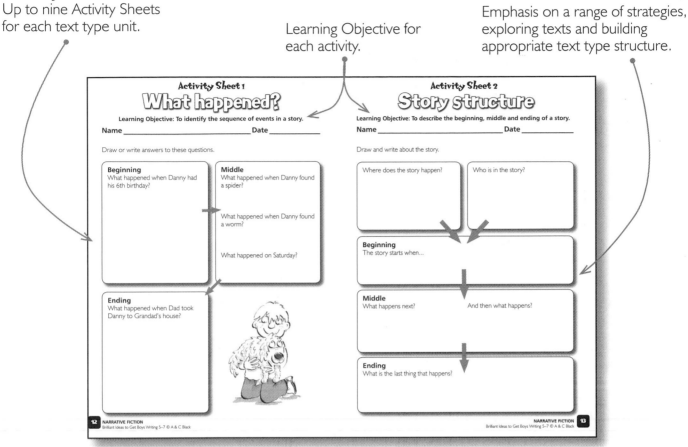

Resource Sheets
Resource Sheets to support and extend engagement with text type.

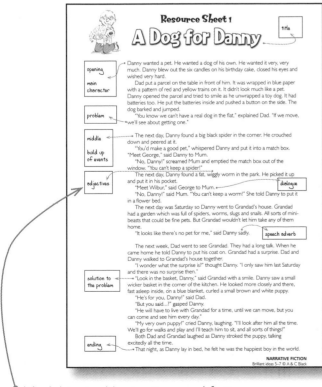

Model text with structure and features highlighted, for display and discussion.

Writing frames to reinforce text structure in text planning.

NARRATIVE FICTION

Narrative fiction is the telling (or narrating) of 'story' using many different forms. It includes the forms of traditional fiction, fold and fairy tales, fables, myths and legends as well as science fiction, fantasy, mystery and adventure, historical and contemporary fiction. Narrative fiction can be presented in many visual forms, including picture books and comic or cartoons.

★ Provide (and read) a range of appropriate texts as models, from genre being studied.

★ Share books which appeal to boys and provide opportunities to respond to them – role-play, dramatisation etc.

★ Provide electronic resources, if appropriate.

★ Create a bank of relevant vocabulary, phrases and prompts which help thinking, planning and reviewing.

★ Use *Talk for writing* principles and lots of opportunity to talk and collaborate prior to and throughout the writing process and dramatic strategies to promote high-quality thinking.

★ Display, demonstrate and discuss model texts and visuals and give a clear purpose for each task. Use genre terminology to ensure clear understanding of text structure and language features.

★ Ensure children discuss and agree text purpose and audience.

★ Provide questions which help the planning process.

★ Make available a range of tools, including ICT tools.

★ Display work in progress and finished work, in many different versions.

★ Ensure opportunites for review and reflection are available and provide effective feedback.

NARRATIVE FICTION

Purpose	to interest and entertain
Structure	events in sequential order; beginning (introducing characters and setting), middle (events and problems) and ending (resolution)
Language features	usually past tense verbs; story book language 'Once there was...'; descriptive language and dialogue; first or third person pronouns
Visual features	often has illustrations, which can support the reader
Examples	*The Tiger who came to Tea*, by Judith Kerr; *Not Now Bernard*, by David McKee; *Horrid Henry* stories by Francesca Simon

Cross-curricular suggestions

Art and design
★ Children represent characters and settings using art and design skills.

Geography
★ Children can explore settings, both imaginary and 'realistic' and use mapping skills to describe them to others.

PSHE
★ Children can discuss events and issues raised in narratives with reference to their own lives.

Teacher's notes

Use the **Challenge Cards** (Resource Sheet 5) to extend the unit.

Activity Sheet 1

Read the model text on Resource Sheet I with the children. Display the questions for reflection on Resource Sheet 2 and ask children to discuss them in small groups. Then display the model again and discuss the structure of the text with the class. Point out the sequence of beginning, middle and ending and identify the characters. Together, highlight the words that show the passing of time, dialogue and descriptive words. Provide the children with the activity sheet. Ask them to work with a partner and draw or write answers to the 'what happened?' questions.

Activity Sheet 2

Discuss stories being read by the class and orally explore 'what happened?' by asking the children to describe what happens in the beginning, middle and ending. Choose a story the children are familiar with and which has a clear structure. Ask them to use the activity sheet to draw or write what happened in each part of the story.

Activity Sheet 3

Talk with the children about the settings of the model text: the flat, the park and Grandad's house. Ask them to think about what Danny might have seen in these places. Display Resource Sheet 3 or give it to children in groups, and use the prompts to describe one of the settings. If time permits give groups time to 'create' or draw each of the settings and display them. Similarly, discuss the settings of stories that are currently being read. What can characters see, hear, smell and feel there? What time of day is it? What is the weather like? Can characters hear anything there? Encourage the children to expand their responses and generate lots of describing words by asking questions. Ask the children to draw and write about a setting from one of their favourite stories using the activity sheet.

Activity Sheet 4

Talk with the children about the characters in the model text: Danny, Dad, Mum and Grandad. Discuss what they think the characters are like, for example: Danny, six years old, an only child perhaps, likes animals; Mum, dislikes mini-beasts; Grandad is kind. Discuss what characters are like in stories that are currently being read and how some stories tell you a lot about the characters and others let you guess what they are like. Ask the children to choose a character they like from one of the stories, close their eyes and picture the character in their mind's eye. Tell them to add details about the character to the activity sheet.

Activity Sheet 5

Display and discuss General Reference sheet 'Planning a story'. Ask the children to write their own version of the story 'A Dog for Danny'. Discuss how they could change the main character, Danny, for a character of their own. Compare the settings the children described in activity 3. Discuss how they could change the setting. Talk about the plot. What could the new character want in their new setting and why can't they get it? How do they overcome the problem? Ask the children to draw and write their new version of the story using the activity sheet to plan it first.

REFLECTION & FEEDBACK suggestions

Discuss how stories tell us 'what happened'. Ask the children to suggest why it is important to have a beginning, middle and ending in stories. Ask them to say which sort of characters they like to write about and why. Similarly, which settings they enjoy describing and why.

GETTING STARTED

Display

Create a display of stories that appeal to boys. Enlist boys from the class to choose which books should be included in the display.

Role-play

Give the children a simple scenario, for example, going shopping. Arrange them in pairs and give them two character cards from Resource Sheet 4. Ask them to role-play going shopping, as the characters on the cards.

Tell me why?

Read a simple story to the children. At strategic points stop the story and ask the children to tell you why something happened or why someone did or said something.

Act and tell

Describe an action to begin a story in the first person and simultaneously act it out, for example, as you act out sweeping the floor, say 'I was sweeping the floor one day when I saw a...' Stop and ask the children to suggest what it was. Choose one of the children to continue the story, act it out and stop at the last word of the sentence. Continue so all the children are included.

Action story circle

Arrange the children into a circle. Using a simple story, rhyme or poem they are all familiar with, ask them to perform another action while they tell the story, for example, standing on one leg, hopping, or patting the top of their head. As soon as a child stops the action or runs out of words, the next child continues the story.

What happened?

Learning Objective: To identify the sequence of events in a story.

Name _____ **Date** _____

Draw or write answers to these questions.

Beginning
What happened when Danny had his 6th birthday?

Middle
What happened when Danny found a spider?

What happened when Danny found a worm?

What happened on Saturday?

Ending
What happened when Dad took Danny to Grandad's house?

Story structure

Learning Objective: To describe the beginning, middle and ending of a story.

Name _____ **Date** _____

Draw and write about the story.

Where does the story happen?	Who is in the story?

Beginning
The story starts when…

Middle
What happens next?   And then what happens?

Ending
What is the last thing that happens?

Activity Sheet 3
Settings

Learning Objective: To describe a story setting.

Name _____ **Date** _____

Draw the setting of the story and add labels. Use the prompts to help you. Write words or a sentence to describe the setting.

What time is it?
sun
moon

What is the weather like?
rain
clouds
wind
sun

What is in the setting?
people
objects
animals
plants and trees

The setting:

The setting is _____

In the place there are _____

The time is _____

The weather is _____

Words I can use to describe the place

NARRATIVE FICTION
Brilliant Ideas to Get Boys Writing 5–7 © A & C Black

Activity Sheet 4
Character

Learning Objective: To add words to describe a story character.

Name _____ **Date** _____

Draw a story character you like. Add words to the circles to tell more about the character.

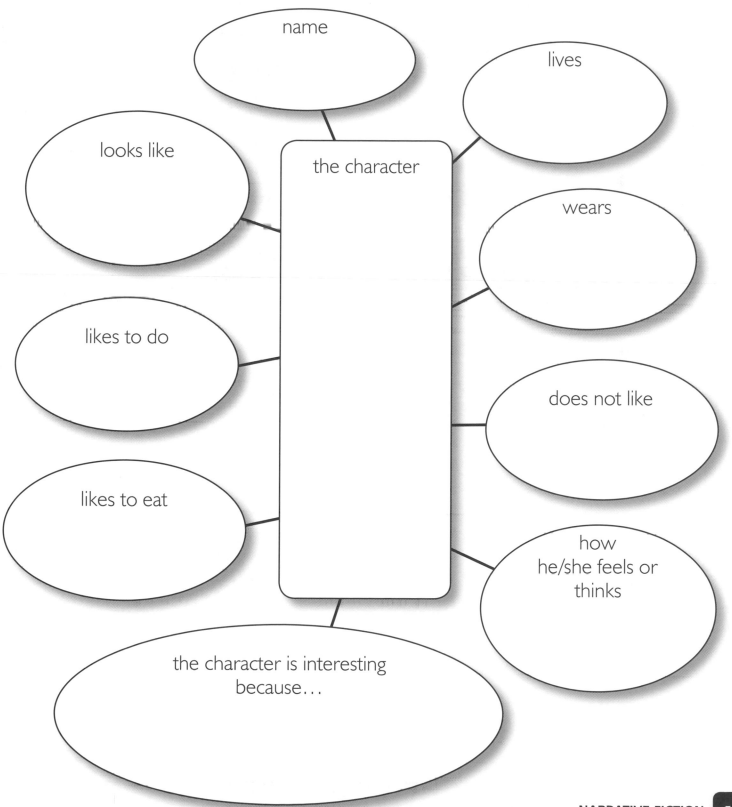

Rewriting the story

Learning Objective: To draw and write a story with a beginning, middle and ending.

Name _____ **Date** _____

Draw and write notes to help you tell a new story.

characters

setting

beginning

middle

ending

FAMILIAR SETTINGS

Purpose	to entertain
Structure	often sequential events; contains a clear beginning, middle and ending, a problem and resolution; written in sections or chapters
Language features	usually past tense, but sometimes in the present tense; descriptive language and dialogue
Visual features	often illustrated
Examples	*Dogger*, by Shirley Hughes; *Burglar Bill* by Allan Ahlberg; *This is Our House* by Michael Rosen

Cross-curricular suggestions

Geography
★ Children can draw story maps or visual plans with labels to illustrate settings and events in stories.

PSHE
★ Encourage children to recognise and challenge stereotypical characters and behaviour in stories through role-playing alternative actions based on story events.

Art & design
★ Children can sketch and draw familiar characters and settings, to illustrate their stories.

Teacher's notes

Use the **Challenge Cards** (Resource Sheet 7) to extend the unit.

Activity Sheet 1

Select an appropriate story to read aloud, one which is set in a familiar environment, with a clear plot and not too many characters. Allow plenty of time for discussion including any parallels the children can identify with their own lives. Introduce the appropriate literacy vocabulary and ask them to consider first the characters; where it takes place; what do they consider the main event to be? Children complete the activity sheet by drawing the people, places and the key event. Focus discussion on the 'familiar' nature of the characters, setting etc.

Activity Sheet 2

After reading a story with a familiar setting together, children should identify four key events in the story. Write a simple sentence to describe each event on sheets of paper. On the board write 'First' then add the sentence about the first event. Write 'Then', 'Next' and 'Finally' and add the appropriate sentence each time. Check with children that they are happy with the sequence. Give pairs of children the activity sheet and ask them to choose another story and complete the sheet together after agreeing the sequence and their sentences. Make a class list of other words to show the passing of time. Delete, if still space problem.

Activity Sheet 3

Discuss recent school and playtime events with the class. Provide children with copies of the activity sheet. Encourage them to discuss the characters and talk with a partner about what these children might do in a playground setting. They then draw pictures to show the sequence of events in their story. Thinking about their own adventures in the playground will help. Some children may be able to write simple sentences to accompany their pictures.

Activity Sheet 4

Talk together about stories that feature football. Ask children if they have read any and to describe what happened. Tell them they are going to make a plan for their own football story. Give them an opportunity to discuss their ideas with a talk partner and focus on characters and setting. Ask them to think about why the story happens i.e. what do the characters want to do? They can then make their notes on the activity sheet.

Activity Sheet 5

This activity continues the planning for a football story. Talk about the need for a beginning, a middle and an ending in stories. Explain that writing notes for the story, clearly showing these stages will help them write exciting stories and that readers will understand the storyline. Invite them to expand their first ideas with a partner and then to write notes and if possible sentences on the activity sheet. Encourage them to use some of the 'good words' they thought of activity 4. Help children to write a polished version of their story.

Activity Sheet 6

Prior to the activity, talk about pets and pet shows and why people enter their pets. How do they feel about this? To help the children understand the humour of the happy ending on the sheet, explain, if necessary, what rescued dogs are, i.e. unwanted pets that are given new homes. Give the activity sheet to pairs of children and give them time to think about the pictures. They fill in the detail by naming the characters, describing what happens and how the story ends.

Activity Sheet 7

Choose a book about 'naughty' younger brothers and sisters, such as *My Naughty Little Sister* by Dorothy Edwards and *Charlie and Lola* by Lauren Child to start a discussion. Ask children if they know any funny or embarrassing family stories about a younger brother or sister. Encourage them to ask at home. Children then tell a partner a family story. Provide them with the activity sheet and ask them to write notes about their partner's story, using 'he' or 'she'. Encourage them to write sentences to tell the story. Display and discuss General Reference Sheet 'Punctuation'.

REFLECTION & FEEDBACK suggestions

Discuss favourite 'familiar setting' stories and make a short list of titles. Conduct a class poll and display the results as a bar graph. Children use post-it notes to comment on titles and display around the graph.

GETTING STARTED

On the cube

As a class, think of 'familiar' characters and settings. Make a list. Use the 'Blank cube' General Reference Sheet for children to draw some of these characters and settings. In groups, throw a character cube and a setting cube, then someone gives a sentence about this character and/or setting.

My favourite place

Ask children to describe their favourite place to a friend. Do they know where it is? They can then write a couple of sentences describing the place, and draw it on the other side of the paper. Post the descriptions on the wall and ask others to guess where it is. How many places were guessed correctly?

Describe a character

Using a computer scan some characters from familiar stories. Ask children to add comments about the character in bubbles around the character. Display and discuss the comments. There is no need for children to 'own' their comments.

Problems and solutions

Make a collection of 'familiar' situations, using photos or magazine images. Scan them on the computer. Put them on the whiteboard one by one and ask children to think of a problem which might arise in the situation and then a solution to that problem.

What's it about?

Display the story titles from Resource Sheet 6 on the CD onto the whiteboard. Ask children, in pairs, to pick one of the titles and tell their partner what they think the story is about. Does the other child agree? Ask some volunteers to tell their story to the class.

Thinking about a familiar story

Learning Objective: To identify parts of a story they have heard.

Name _____ **Date** _____

Think about the story you have just heard.

Who were the main characters? Draw them here.

Do you know people like these characters?

What was the setting? Draw it here.

Do you know a setting like this?

What was the main event? Draw it here.

Has this happened to you, or someone you know?

Has anything like this happened to you?

What happened?

Learning Objective: To identify the sequence of events in a story.

Name _____ **Date** _____

What happened in the story? Write a sentence or draw a picture in each box.

Title

First	Next

Then	Finally

Activity Sheet 3
In the playground

Learning Objective: To make notes about a character's actions in a familiar setting.

Name _____ **Date** _____

Draw or write your story ideas on the sheet.

Characters in my story.

My name is . . . .   My name is . . . .   My name is . . . .

What happens?

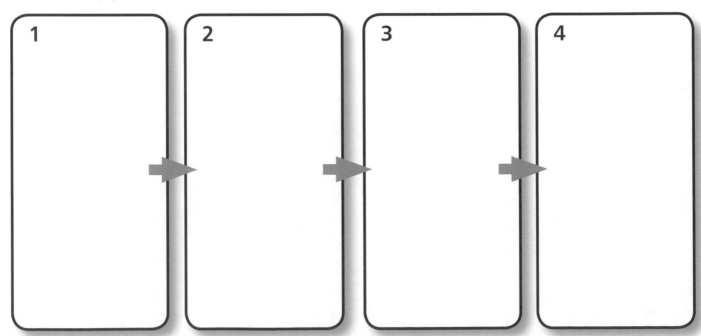

| 1 | 2 | 3 | 4 |

Activity Sheet 4
Planning a story

Learning Objective: To make notes about character, setting and plot.

Name _____ **Date** _____

Make notes of your ideas for a football story in the frame.

Who is in your story?

Good words to describe them:

Where does your story happen?

Good words to describe it:

Why does your story happen?

What do the characters want to do?

What events stop this happening?

What do the characters do to make it happen at last?

Activity Sheet 5
What happened?

Learning Objective: To show a clear beginning, middle and ending.

Name _____ Date _____

Write some sentences for the beginning, middle and ending of your football story.

Beginning:
Who and where?

Middle:
Events   *Reasons for events*

Ending:
Last event   *Reason for event*

How do they feel at the end?

Activity Sheet 6
The dog show

Learning objective: To write sentences to tell a story.

Name _____ Date _____

Look at the pictures on the left. Write two or more sentences for each picture.

1: Who is the boy? Give him a name. What is his dog called? Where were they going?

2: What happened? How did the boy feel? What did he say? Write it in the speech bubble.

3: Who is the man? What did he do?

4: What happened at the end? How did the boy feel then?

Activity Sheet 7
Bad behaviour!

Learning Objective: To make notes for a story about their partner.

Name_____ **Date**_____

Who?	Where?	What?

When _____ was younger …

_____

_____

_____

_____

_____

_____

_____

_____

_____

_____

_____

_____

_____

_____

DIFFERENT CULTURES

Purpose	to entertain and inform about different cultures
Structure	sequential events; a clear beginning, middle and ending; often in chapters or sections
Language features	usually past tense; descriptive language and authentic details; first or third person
Visual features	often illustrated
Examples	*The Colour of Home* by Mary Hoffman; *Handa's Surprise* by Eileen Browne; *Bringing the Rain to Kapiti Plane* by Verna Aardema

Cross-curricular suggestions

Geography
★ Children find places on an atlas or globe.
★ Use discussion for children to compare similarities and differences in different locations.

Citizenship/PSHE
★ Children explore how people live in different parts of the world.

Science
★ Children learn about food from around the world.

Teacher's notes

Use the **Challenge Cards** (Resource Sheet 12) to extend the unit.

Activity Sheet 1

Read a story that contrasts their own setting and culture with that of a different one, for example, *The Colour of Home* by Mary Hoffman or *Handa's Hen* by Eileen Browne. Together, draw up lists of similarities and differences. Give children the activity sheet and talk about the setting, then ask children in pairs to draw or write what is the same and what is different about the setting compared to their own local setting. Alternatively display Resource Sheets 8 & 9 and discuss the similarities and differences in class or ask children to discuss with a partner. Use discussion prompts on Resource Sheet 10.

Activity Sheet 2

Discuss the characters, including animal characters, children have read about in traditional stories or stories from other cultures. If time permits, encourage children to find appropriate books, show the characters to a partner and describe the characters. Revisit one of the setting pictures on Resource Sheets 8 & 9. Invite the children to imagine a character they would like to see in a story in one of the settings. Ask them to add words and phrases that describe the

character on the activity sheet. Encourage them to think not just about appearance but about likes, dislikes, feelings and actions.

Activity Sheet 3

Display the character images from Resource Sheet 11. Ask the children to suggest a setting for each of the characters. Discuss what sort of activities the character would do each day. Invite children to write one or more sentences about the character on the activity sheet.

Activity Sheet 4

Use a shared writing session to demonstrate how to make notes to plan a story in a setting from another culture. Remind the children of the work they have done to describe the differences in settings and characters in the first three activities. Discuss how the setting would affect what happens. Explain that they are going to plan a story that is set in a jungle and, in small groups, give them the chance to role-play being in this setting. Provide the children with the activity sheet (if possible copy to A3) and ask them to role-play the journey then make notes of words or phrases to describe what might happen to the character as he travels from the start to the end.

Activity Sheet 5

In this activity, ask the children to combine the work they have done in the first four activities and write their jungle story, possibly with a partner or an adult, using the activity sheet. Some children can draw the story and add key words. Ask the children to share their stories orally.

REFLECTION & FEEDBACK suggestions

Talk about characters and settings in stories from other cultures. Ask the children to say what they would find strange or difficult if they were in one of the settings. Ask them to say what a character from another culture might find strange or difficult if they were in the children's own setting and culture.

 Role-play

Display the different settings on Resource Sheets 8 & 9 or settings from books the children know. Ask the children, in small groups, to role-play walking through each setting.

Hot seat

Choose a character from a story about another culture that the children are familiar with. Choose children to sit in the hot seat as the character. The other children ask questions about what life is like, what the character sees and hears and what they eat.

Compare

Read two stories with similar structures but different settings to the children, for example, *This is the House that Jack Built*, and *Bringing the Rain to Kapiti Plain*. Ask the children to role-play the actions which form each story and show how they are different in each different setting.

Book display

With the children, create a book display of stories from different cultures that they have enjoyed or think they might enjoy. Suggest they recommend one of the stories they have enjoyed to a friend.

Talk together

Talk about how the culture and way of life is similar and different in different parts of the world. Provide the children with different setting descriptions orally, for example, 'This place is hot. It rains every day. There are lots of wild animals.' Invite the children to say what would be different about their life in the setting.

Learn about

Have any of the children lived in other countries (or have family in other countries)? Ask these children to talk to the class about their own experiences or those they have heard about from family members. Invite a parent, grandparent or carer who has lived or worked in other countries to come in and talk to the children about life there.

What is it like here?

Learning Objective: To generate vocabulary to describe settings from other cultures.

Name _____ Date _____

Look at the pictures of a story setting. What is the same as in a story set where you live? What is different?

The same		Different

Activity Sheet 2
What am I like?

Learning Objective: To choose words and phrases to describe a character.

Name _____ Date _____

What character would you put into your setting? You can make up one of your own or use a character from another story. Draw the character and write words and phrases to describe the character.

Looks like:

hair

eyes

skin

Clothes:

Eats:

Moves around:

Likes:

Hates:

Activity Sheet 3
What do I do?

Learning Objective: To write a sentence about a character from a different culture.

Name _____ **Date** _____

What do you think this character does each day? Finish the sentences about the character.

When I get up...

For breakfast I eat...

After breakfast I go ....

All morning I ....

In the afternoon I ....

For supper I eat..

I go to sleep on..

What happens here?

Learning Objective: To make notes about a story in a different setting.

Name _____ **Date** _____

Look carefully at the picture and the characters. Make notes on the picture as the boy travels through the jungle. Who does he meet? What do they say to each other? What does he see? How does he move? What happens at the end?

Activity Sheet 5
Jungle story

Learning Objective: To make notes about a story in a different setting.

Name _____ **Date** _____

Write or draw your jungle story. Think about what happens in the beginning, middle and ending.

Jungle story	
Beginning Who? Where?	
Middle Who? What? Where? When?	
Ending What happened? Where? When? How do they feel now?	

DIFFERENT CULTURES
Brilliant Ideas to Get Boys Writing 5–7 © A & C Black

TRADITIONAL STORIES

Purpose	to entertain; to convey a message
Structure	simple plot; sequence of events; clearly defined conflict and resolution; often begin 'once upon a time'
Language features	past tense; limited descriptions; often repetition of words and phrases; important themes such as honesty and hard work often included
Visual features	often illustrated
Examples	*Jack and the Beanstalk*; *Robin Hood*; *Aladdin*; *Puss in Boots*

Cross-curricular suggestions

History
★ Children can discuss the lack of modern technology in these traditional stories and consider differences between life in the past and their own lives.

Maths
★ Children could explore the way that many traditional stories feature 'magic' numbers, usually three or seven.

Geography
★ Children draw and label settings or journeys from traditional stories as maps.

Teacher's notes

Use the **Challenge Cards** (Resource Sheet 18) to extend the unit.

Activity Sheet 1

Make a list of traditional stories. Talk about the language that features in traditional stories, 'Once upon a time', 'Far, far away' and so on. Write the words on the board or use Resource Sheet 13. Invite the children to choose one story and act it out with a partner, using story language. Invite the children to complete the activity sheet, drawing key events and writing sentences or key words (in story language) to retell the story.

Activity Sheet 2

Ask the children to select a character from a traditional story and recall all the information they can about their personality and appearance. Ask for volunteers to sit in the hot seat in the role of a character and encourage the others to ask questions. Make notes of character traits which emerge. Then ask children to choose a character and complete the activity sheet. Children can read their descriptions aloud and ask others to guess who it is.

Activity Sheet 3

Talk about the settings of traditional stories – in the historical past. Using an illustration, describe the features of the setting. Talk about the place, the animals, rural or town, the time of day and year. Ask children to describe the setting on the sheet orally and to write descriptive sentences about it. Ask them to share some events that may take place there with a partner. Use Resource Sheet 14 to tell a tale to a partner.

Activity Sheet 4

Read or tell the story of 'Jack and the Beanstalk' (Resource Sheets 15 & 16). Discuss the characters and the setting. In groups, children discuss the four events identified in the story and make a note of why each happened and what happened as a result, e.g: Jack's mother threw out the beans so a giant beanstalk grew. Give the sheet to each group and ask them to complete it together.

Activity Sheet 5

Revisit the opening of the story (Resource Sheet 15) and mark the traditional story language and character details. Together plan another version of *Jack and the Beanstalk*. Task the children to think of a new event to add to the story and to think of sentences which encourage the reader to read on. Children then write their own tale about Jack and the beanstalk, with their new event. It may help if they can tell their story to a partner first.

Activity Sheet 6

Ensure children are familiar with *The Three Billy Goats Gruff*. An enlarged photocopy of the sheet might help some children. Place the children in groups of four and ask them to work together to read the script and discuss what happens next before completing the worksheet. Invite the groups to perform their completed plays.

Activity Sheet 7

Remind the children about the language used to open and end traditional stories. Provide them with the activity sheet and ask them to suggest how they would begin the comic strip story, and end it. Ask the children to draw a beginning, middle and ending of their own story and write a sentence to begin and end it.

Activity Sheet 8

Write some speech bubbles together then use Resource Sheet 17 to see how to change them to punctuated sentences. Provide the activity sheet and ask children to role-play what the characters might be saying with a partner. Invite them to write in the speech bubbles and then write the speech in punctuated sentences.

Activity Sheet 9

Read some alternative versions of traditional story, for example, *The True Story of the Three Little Pigs*, or *The Frog Prince Continued*, by John Scieszka. Arrange the children into groups of four. Ask each to take a role from the *Goldilocks* story, and through role-play, experiment with changing the story, for example, not all the bears go for a walk, so Goldilocks gets a shock; Goldilocks and baby bear become best friends; the bears eat Goldilocks instead of the porridge! Ask them to write their new version of *Goldilocks* on the activity sheet.

REFLECTION & FEEDBACK suggestions

Draw up a list of favourite characters from traditional stories. Ask the children to describe what makes them into favourites. Hold a class vote and make a graph showing least favourite to most favourite.

Getting Started

Guess the story

Play a game where you or a volunteer acts out a character from a traditional tale and uses the character's repeated words, such as 'I'll huff and I'll puff...' 'What big ears you have...' and so on. Ask the others to name the story.

My version

Ask children to draw traditional characters and settings onto two blank cubes (made from the General Reference Sheet 'Blank cube' on the CD). In groups, children throw a character cube and a setting cube and then make up a sentence about the character in that setting.

Where is it?

Display a traditional story setting. Ask children to guess where it might be and to justify their guesses. Take lots of guesses, before revealing the setting.

Baddy hot seat

Create some name cards for traditional story baddies, for example, the wolf from 'Red Riding Hood', or 'The Three Little Pigs', the ogre from 'The Three Billy Goats Gruff', and so on. Children pick a card, sit in the hot seat and describe the events from the baddy's point of view.

Watch it

Watch traditional stories on DVD or YouTube. Ask the children in small groups to recreate the story and film them with a digital camera, or take stills and make a display.

Activity Sheet 1
Telling a story

Learning Objective: To retell a story in sequence using story language.

Name _____ Date _____

Tell the story here in pictures and words.

1

Once upon a time… _____

_____

_____

2

Suddenly… _____

_____

_____

3

Then… _____

_____

_____

4

_____

_____

…and they all lived happily ever after.

TRADITIONAL STORIES
Brilliant Ideas to Get Boys Writing 5–7 © A & C Black

Guess who!

Learning Objective: To describe a story character.

Name _____ **Date** _____

Draw your character in the frame.

Answer the questions and describe your character.

Word box:

tiny	scared
big	clothes
small	rags
giant	fur
brave	

How big is your character? _____

What does he wear? _____

Is he happy, sad or funny? _____

Is your character brave? _____

Is he is friendly or fierce? _____

Does he help or scare people? _____

Would you like to meet him? _____

Where did it happen?

Learning Objective: To use descriptive phrases when describing setting.

Name _____ **Date** _____

Look at the setting for a story. Write about the time, the place and the things you see. Talk with a partner about some of the events that might happen and make a list of them.

_____

_____

_____

_____

_____

_____

_____

Jack and the Beanstalk

Learning Objective: To make notes about characters, setting and events in a traditional story.

Name _____ **Date** _____

Make notes about your traditional story.

Who are the characters?	*Where* does it happen?
What are the events and why do they happen? **1**	**2**
3	**4**
How does it end?	

Activity Sheet 5
A new tale!

Learning Objective: To make notes for a new event in a traditional story.

Name _____ **Date** _____

Make some notes of your ideas for a new story about 'Jack and the Beanstalk'.
Write some sentences for the beginning, middle and ending of your story.

Who are the characters?	**Where does your story happen?**
Good words to describe them:	Good words to describe

Beginning
Think of a good sentence to begin

Middle
List all the events in your story

Ending
Think of a good ending sentence

A play about the 'Three Billy Goats Gruff'

Learning Objective: To retell a story in drama form and write an ending.

Name _____ **Date** _____

Troll: Who is that crossing over my bridge?

Little Billy Goat Gruff: It is me, Little Billy Goat Gruff.

Troll: I am going to eat you up!

Little Billy Goat Gruff: Please don't eat me. I am only little. Wait for my brother.

Troll: Who is that crossing over my bridge?

Middle Size Billy Goat Gruff: It is me, Middle Size Billy Goat Gruff.

Troll: I am going to eat you up!

Middle Size Billy Goat Gruff: Please don't eat me. I am only little. Wait for my brother.

Troll:

Big Billy Goat Gruff:

Troll:

Big Billy Goat Gruff:

Beginnings and endings

Learning Objective: To write a beginning and an ending for a story.

Name _____ **Date** _____

Look at the beginning, middle and ending of the traditional story. Now draw the beginning, middle and ending of your own story. Write a sentence to begin your story and another one to end it, under the pictures.

beginning

middle

ending

Opening sentence

Ending sentence

Activity Sheet 8
Dialogue

Learning Objective: To write simple character dialogue.

Name _____ **Date** _____

What are they saying? Write what the characters are saying in the speech bubbles.

Now write the the speech in sentences using punctuation.

_____

_____

_____

_____

_____

_____

_____

What really happened to Goldilocks and the three bears?

Learning Objective: To write own version of a traditional story.

Name _____ **Date** _____

What else might happen to Goldilocks? Write the opening of the story, then continue the story in the boxes. How does the story end? Write an ending at the bottom.

Beginning

Then

1

2

3

Ending

FaNTaSY WORLDS

Purpose	to entertain and amuse
Structure	real and imagined settings; characters with magical and human characteristics; sequence of imagined events; written in chapters or sections
Language features	strong description to create vivid setting, characters and events; dialogue appropriate to characters
Visual features	often has illustrations
Examples	*The Magic Bed* by John Burningham; *Hugo Pepper* by Chris Riddell; *The Emperor of Absurdia* by Chris Riddell; *Tom and the Island of Dinosaurs* by Ian Beck

Cross-curricular suggestions

English
★ Visit the library to find a selection of books set in fantasy worlds to read to the class. Encourage boys to review them by skim reading them and viewing the images.

History
★ Children identify typical historical events portrayed in stories. They list both real and imagined objects and actions, for example knight and dragon stories.

Art
★ Discuss and explore possible settings around a theme by asking students to paint large scenes as a background for wall stories. Encourage them to use different media for background and detail.

Teacher's notes

Use the **Challenge Cards** (Resource Sheet 24) to extend the unit.

Activity Sheet 1

Select a fantasy story and a realistic story to read aloud – if possible with a boy character. Allow time to discuss the characters, setting and events after each story. Children complete the activity sheet in pairs. When they have finished, ask them to join with another pair and discuss the differences between the 'real' and the 'fantasy' stories. Make a class list of books which fit into both categories.

Activity Sheet 2

Look at the class list of books for the two categories and talk together about how events and actions are similar and different between familiar and fantasy stories. Ask the children to choose one story from each setting and compare them using the activity sheet.

Activity Sheet 3

Look at illustrations from fantasy books on children's list. If possible, scan a setting illustration and display on the whiteboard. Ask children to give you as many words to describe the setting as they can think of and discuss their words. Make a list for reference. In pairs, children describe the settings on the sheet and label parts if they want. Remind them that they can use made up words. Role-play being characters in one of the settings.

Activity Sheet 4

Talk about how authors and artists describe in words and illustration places no-one has visited or seen. Read some examples and make a list of author's descriptive words for children to use. Ask them to choose their own fantasy world and to draw a picture of it with labels on the activity sheet. Encourage them to add good words to describe the setting and write a description.

Activity Sheet 5

Characters in fantasy worlds are often set against each other - knight (good), dragon (bad). Ask children to list some good characters and some bad characters they know. Ask them to invent a good and a bad character of their own, describe them and list what they will do in a story on the activity sheet.

Activity Sheet 6

Fantasy characters use English as their spoken language, but sometimes they add other words or sounds, for example 'Fee fi fo fum'. Ask children, in pairs, to decide upon two fantasy characters and then to role-play a dialogue between them. (They can use Resource Sheet 20 to describe their characters.) They could tape their conversation and use the recording to help them write the dialogue on the activity sheet.

Activity Sheet 7

Discuss the different ways in which characters move in fantasy worlds: people able to fly, or travel under water; flying horses and dragons; magic carpets. Choose one example from the activity sheet or Resource Sheet 21 and discuss how the action can be conveyed in words. Together, draw up a list of good adverbs and adjectives that help to convey movement and action. Encourage the children to think of onomatopoeic words and to describe the pictures of movement on the activity sheet.

Activity Sheet 8

Display the model text (Resource Sheet 22) and read it aloud. Find words and phrases that tell readers about the setting. Identify the beginning and the middle of the story. Ask the children to say what goes wrong, i.e. the first problem and then what else goes wrong, i.e. a complication. How is the problem solved? Identify the ending. Ask the children to find words and phrases the author has used to add detail and interest to the story, i.e. action verbs, adjectives. Provide groups with the activity sheet and ask them to choose a setting and write ideas for the beginning, middle and ending of a story.

Activity Sheet 9

Good stories always have a problem to be resolved. Discuss some problems and solutions children can think of. Display Resource Sheet 23 and discuss together. Give children the activity sheet and ask them to write notes for all the elements of their own fantasy story, they can use the setting from the previous activity.

REFLECTION & FEEDBACK suggestions

Respond to the imaginative and creative ideas. Work with children to publish their stories using ICT, for sharing with each other and another class.

GETTING STARTED

Images

Set aside time to view and discuss images of a range of fantasy worlds. Expand boys' own imagination by exposing them to the work of many illustrators depicting the same settings.

Word bank

Develop word banks for describing a range of fantasy settings and characters. Continue to add to these lists through reading and discussion, throughout the unit of work.

Who am I?

Play 'Who am I?' with some of the well-known fantasy characters. Ask children to jot down three or four clues for others to guess. They might also wear something that helps identify the character.

Role-play

Arrange children in groups of three. Cut out the cards on Resource sheet 19 and mix them up. Place them upside down in three piles – character; setting; problem — and ask the group to pick a card from each pile. Ask them to look closely at the cards and discuss how to work out a story featuring the elements on each card. Ask them to role-play their ideas.

Murals

Paint large murals of one or two fantasy worlds to use as a backdrop for oral storytelling and writing. Cut out photographs of pupils role-playing a character and place them on the mural to show a scene from a story.

Sounds and noises

Review literature to identify and list the way sounds are written in stories. For example, 'ARRGH!!!'. Tell children that the spelling matches the sounds of letters to the sound of the noise. Encourage them to invent some of their own.

Activity Sheet 1
Fantasy or real?

Learning Objective: To identify the difference between fantasy and real story elements.

Name _____ Date _____

Make a list of the 'fantasy' and 'real' story elements using the headings.

FANTASY WORLDS
Brilliant Ideas to Get Boys Writing 5–7 © A & C Black

Same or different?

Learning Objective: To compare a story set in real life with one set in a fantasy world.

Name _____ **Date** _____

Select TWO stories you have read – one about real life and the other about a fantasy world. Draw and write what each story is about.

Title		
Author		
Where?		
Who?		
What?		
Ending		
What is the same?		
What is different?		
I like… because…		

Activity Sheet 3
What's it like?

Learning Objective: To describe a fantasy setting.

Name _____ Date _____

Describe these fantasy worlds. Write as many good descriptive words as you can.
Label the things you can see in each fantasy world.

_____
_____
_____
_____
_____
_____
_____
_____
_____
_____
_____

THIS WAY UP

DISCO

OUTER SPACE

_____
_____
_____
_____
_____
_____
_____
_____
_____
_____

Where am I?

Learning Objective: To make notes about characters for a story, before writing a polished version.

Name _____ **Date** _____

Draw a picture of a fantasy world. Add labels to describe it. Write a list of good descriptive words.

Fantasy World

Wow! words to use:	Write a description of your fantasy world
	_____
	_____
	_____
	_____
	_____
	_____

Brilliant Ideas to Get Boys Writing 5–7 © A & C Black

Activity Sheet 5
Good or bad?

Learning Objective: To identify 'good' and 'bad' character stereotypes in stories.

Name _____ **Date** _____

Choose a good and a bad character. Write their name or draw them in the boxes. Use the prompts to write something about them.

Good character

Do they have special powers?

Why are they good?

What can they do?

Bad character

Do they try to hurt others?

Why are they bad?

What do they do?

_____   _____
_____   _____
_____   _____
_____   _____
_____   _____
_____   _____
_____   _____

FANTASY WORLDS
Brilliant Ideas to Get Boys Writing 5–7 © A & C Black

Activity Sheet 6
What did he say?

Learning Objective: To write simple character dialogue.

Name _____ **Date** _____

Choose two fantasy characters. Write what the characters say to each other.

Draw their faces to show how they feel.

Use sentences with speech marks to show who is speaking.

1 _____

2 _____

_____

1 _____

2 _____

_____

Activity Sheet 7
On the move

Learning Objective: To use imaginative language to describe how characters move in fantasy stories.

Name _____ **Date** _____

Look at each picture from a fantasy world. How can you describe the movement? Write words and phrases to give readers a picture in their mind's eye.

What sounds does the carpet make?

What sounds can the children hear?

What do the children feel?

What do the children see?

Movement words:

What sounds does the jet-board make?

What sounds can the boy hear?

What does the boy feel?

What does the boy see?

Movement words:

Activity Sheet 8
What happened?

Learning Objective: To explore a fantasy plot, looking at beginning, middle and ending.

Name _____ Date _____

Choose one of these settings and write what happened in your story.

	Outer space	Under the sea	Land of dragons
Beginning How does your story begin? Where is your story set and who is in it?			
Middle What happens in this fantasy world? What happens next? What happens after that?			
Ending How does it end?			

What happened?

Learning Objective: To explore a series of events in a story set in a fantasy world.

Name _____ **Date** _____

Write your own story set in a fantasy world. Think about each part of the story.

Characters

Setting

How does it begin?

What happens?

How does the problem happen?

What is the problem?

How is it solved?

How does it end?

Illustrate the fantasy world of your story on another sheet of paper.

EXTENDED NARRATIVES

Purpose	to entertain, to tell a longer story
Structure	usually sequential, may contain flashbacks; clear beginning, middle and end, with plot and sub-plots; often additional problems and resolutions
Language features	usually past tense verbs; descriptive language and dialogue
Visual features	may contain illustrations
Examples	*Bill's New Frock* by Anne Fine; *Flat Stanley* by Jeff Browne; *The Julian Stories* by Anne Cameron

Cross-curricular suggestions

Art
★ Children draw or paint characters and scenes from an extended story.

Drama
★ Children role-play events from an extended story.

ICT
★ Children use ICT to write their chapters in an extended story.

Teacher's notes

Use the **Challenge Cards** (Resource Sheet 26) to extend the unit.

Activity Sheet 1

Discuss the main plot of a story the children are familiar with. For example, in the story *Flat Stanley* by Jeff Brown, the main plot concerns Stanley and if or how he can get back to normal. Ask the children what other problems Stanley meets in the course of the story. (His brother is jealous of the attention; the museum thieves etc.) If unfamiliar with *Flat Stanley*, relate the questioning to a story the children are familiar with. Talk about how these sub plots and extra problems keep readers interested in the story. You can use the stimulus questions on Resource Sheet 25. Ask the children to choose a story they have enjoyed (or use the class novel) and using the activity sheet, write down the extra problems and sub plots for each chapter. In groups, discuss the children's ideas for a plot for a group story to be written in chapters. Use the activity sheet to record their ideas for the main plot and sub plots.

Activity Sheet 2

Within each group, plan characters for the story. Ask each group member to take one character and use the activity sheet to make notes about the character's name, appearance, age, likes and dislikes, ways of moving and speaking. Explain that when writers explore every aspect of a character, the character is more 'real'. Ask them to fill in the speech bubble with a phrase or sentence that is typical of the way their character speaks.

Activity Sheet 3

Arrange the children into pairs or groups of three. Ask them to take the role of the character they planned in activity 2 and role-play a conversation for the group story. Encourage them to use an informal tone with, perhaps, interjections such as 'Wow!', 'But...' and so on to make the conversation realistic. Children could record the conversations, which will help when they come to write them. Ask the pairs or groups to collaborate to write their conversation using the activity sheet.

Activity Sheet 4

Refer the children to their initial ideas for a plot and sub plots for the story from activity 1. Enlarge a copy of this activity sheet and ask the group to fill in a story map to use for an overview of the whole story.

Activity Sheet 5

Discuss the group plan for a story in chapters. Together draw up a plan to show the number of chapters, the main event in each chapter, the setting for each chapter and which characters appear or are introduced in each chapter. Share the chapters between the group members and ask them to plan their chapter on the activity sheet and then write a draft and then a final version. (Some children may find using the computer easier.) Display the finished story.

REFLECTION & FEEDBACK suggestions

Collect the children's chapters and put them together. Read the class story aloud. Identify which chapters need further work and why.

GETTING STARTED

Speech bubbles

Paint a large background setting for the group story. Ask the children to each paint a picture of a character. Cut them out and stick them onto the setting background. Children can add speech bubbles to the characters during the course of writing the group story.

Thought bubbles

Find examples of dialogue in the class novel or other stories the children have read. Ask the children to suggest what the characters are thinking instead of what they are saying.

'Cliff hanger' chapter endings

Invite groups or pairs of children to freeze frame the chapter endings and describe what will happen next. Ask children to mime key moments from a story and the others try to guess what is happening. When a child guesses correctly, they take up the story and mime another part.

Take up the story

Taking turns in a group, ask the children to describe what happened in the class novel, chapter by chapter, or use other stories with which the children are familiar. When one child has described the events of one chapter, another child takes up the story.

Phone a friend

Ask the children, at key moments in a story, to phone a friend or relative in the role of one of the characters from the story, describe what is happening or ask for help.

Extra problems

Learning Objective: To identify sub plots in a story.

Name _____ Date _____

Write the main problem of the story. Add any other problems from each chapter in the smaller bubbles. Add more bubbles if you need them.

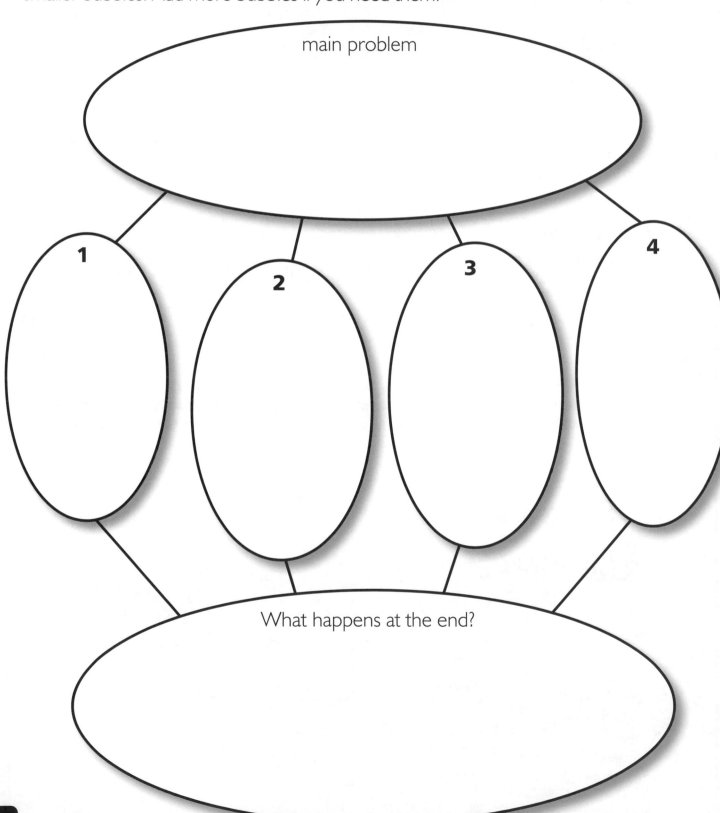

main problem

1

2

3

4

What happens at the end?

EXTENDED NARRATIVES

Character and dialogue

Learning Objective: To plan a character for a group story.

Name _____ Date _____

Write key words and phrases to describe your character. Add as much detail as you can. Write something the character might say in the speech bubble.

Name:

Age:
When is the character's birthday?

What does the character look like?

Six things the character likes.

1 _____
2 _____
3 _____
4 _____
5 _____
6 _____

Six things the character dislikes.

1 _____
2 _____
3 _____
4 _____
5 _____
6 _____

How does the character move?

How does the character speak? What things does the character say?

Activity Sheet 3
Dialogue

Learning Objective: To write a dialogue between two or three characters.

Name _____ **Date** _____

With your partners, write your role-play dialogue. Each of you write your own words from the role-play. Remember to use the character's name, (not 'I'), speech marks and speech verbs. Write in the third person (he or she).

| Character 1 | Character 2 | Character 3 |

| Character 1 | Character 2 | Character 3 |

| Character 1 | Character 2 | Character 3 |

EXTENDED NARRATIVES
Brilliant Ideas to Get Boys Writing 5–7 © A & C Black

Mapping the story

Learning Objective: To plan a story map for an extended story.

Name _____ **Date** _____

With your group, add notes to show 'who, what, where AND WHEN' for each chapter of your group story. Add extra bubbles if needed.

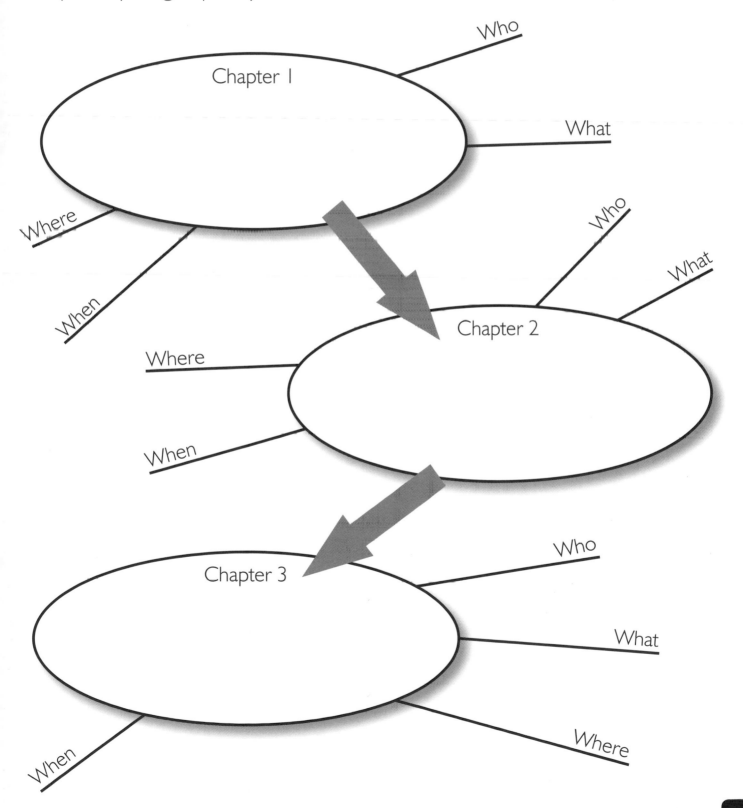

The chapters

Learning Objective: To make notes and write a chapter for a group extended story.

Name _____ **Date** _____

Write or draw your ideas for the chapter first, then use them to write a finished version.

Setting(s)	Characters from the chapter before this one.	New character(s)

Make notes about what happens in this chapter.

What might happen in the next chapter?

How does your chapter end? Try to make it a cliff hanger so readers will want to find out what happens next (unless you have the last chapter).

POETRY

Purpose	to entertain; to stimulate the imagination; to make you look at something in a different way
Structure	varied forms; rhyming or non-rhyming; rhythmical; may be written in verses
Language features	may contain rhyme; may include imaginative or unusual uses of language such as simile, metaphor, alliteration, onomatopoeia
Visual features	may reflect the shape of the subject
Examples	limericks; acrostic poems; shape poems; Haiku; kennings; ballads

Cross-curricular suggestions

ICT
★ Children can write poems using a computer. They can use word art to create calligrams.

Music
★ Children can explore chants and musical rhymes and then add music to their own poems.

PSHE
★ Children can read poems about family and friends, then write poems to add to a 'poetry house' for friends and family.

Teacher's notes

Use the **Challenge Cards** (Resource Sheet 29) to extend the unit.

Activity Sheet 1

Ask the children to write an 'autobiographical' poem about themselves using the activity sheet. Give children the opportunity to 'recite' their poem in assembly, if they want to, and use them in a class display.

Activity Sheet 2

This activity could follow on from activity 1 using a similar pattern. Explain how the Nordic origin of kenning poems arose and how Vikings gave names to their weapons e.g. 'skull splitter' means an axe. Read some examples of kennings to the children and ask them to identify the pattern of nouns/verbs in each line. Encourage the children to write a kenning about themselves and a friend using the activity sheet. Encourage them to cut out each line and experiment with the effect of mixing the lines up.

Activity Sheet 3

Model how to write an acrostic poem using the letters of a word to begin each line, using alliterative adjectives, for example, 'Henry' – Happy, Hungry; Eager, Edgy; Normal, Naughty; Round, Ridiculous; Yellow, Yawning. Encourage the children to write an acrostic poem using their own name on the activity sheet. You might like to suggest alternative names for children with lengthy names.

Activity Sheet 4

The children write a seven line acrostic poem about a friend. Each line begins with the letters of the word 'friend'. Encourage them to add a final line of their own to round off the poem. In this activity, explain that they do not need to use alliteration and are not restricted to a pattern of verb/noun or noun/verb, but can write as many words for each line as they wish.

Activity Sheet 5

Display the shape template for a shape poem from Resource Sheets 27 & 28. Ask the children to suggest words and phrases that could be used to describe the dinosaur and write them inside the shape to model how to create a shape poem. Experiment with combining their suggestions in unusual ways for effect. Provide the children with newspapers, magazines, comics and the activity sheet, photocopied to A3 if necessary. Ask them to work in a group and cut out words and phrases to use for a shape poem about a dinosaur, then glue them inside the shape.

Activity Sheet 6

Read some poems that feature onomatopoeia with the children. Encourage them to suggest onomatopoeic words to describe things, such as walking in mud and so on. Ask the children to write onomatopoeic phrases or sentences for the words on the activity sheet.

REFLECTION & FEEDBACK suggestions

Ask children to read the kennings they wrote about a friend and encourage the others to guess who it is about. Invite the children to say which poem they enjoyed writing most and why.

Getting Started

Alliterate!

Write a group poem about a topic (for example, pirates or tigers) by asking the children to think of three adjectives that begin with the same letter. Write the topic three times on the board then take the children's suggestions to write lines of three alliterative adjectives, ending with the topic word. Ask children to create and illustrate their own and display these in the classroom.

Mix and match

Provide the children with a selection of magazines and newspapers. Encourage them to cut out words and phrases and experiment with putting odd or unusual words/phrases together to create unusual images. Explain that a lot of song-writers have written successful song lyrics by doing this.

Template

Use poems as templates to write a group poem, for example, The Magic Box by Kit Wright. Ask the children to suggest what they would keep in the magic box.

Tongue twisters

Introduce the children to a variety of tongue twisters. Encourage them to make up tongue twisters of their own.

Limericks

Invite the children to make up limericks about themselves using their own first names in the first line.

Role-play

Encourage the children to role-play characters from nursery rhymes and familiar short poems.

Activity Sheet 1
All about me

Learning Objective: To write an autobiographical poem.

Name _____ **Date** _____

Write a poem about yourself where each line has only two words. Follow the prompts on the page.

Begin with a colour word e.g.
black hair
brown eyes
red lips
white teeth

_____

_____

_____

_____

Likes _____

Hates _____

Eats _____

Drinks _____

Wants _____

Needs _____

Equals ME!

Add one word to each line

Kenning

Learning Objective: To write two kennings.

Name _____ **Date** _____

Describe yourself in a five line kenning poem using a verb and a noun on each line. Then interview your partner and write a kenning about him.

Me

Noun	Verb

My friend

Noun	Verb

Acrostic poems

Learning Objective: To generate alliterative adjectives.

Name_____ Date _____

Write an acrostic poem using your name.
Write your name in large letters down the left side of the page. Now add two adjectives beside each letter that begin with the letter on each line.

Jumping, jolly
Active, amusing
Cheerful, cheeky
Kind, kissable.

Clever, cuddly
Helpful, happy,
Rough, ready
Impish, impossible
Sneaky, sly.

Cool, calm
Alert, astonished
Ready, ragged
Loud, lively
Outdoor, organised.

Silly, slow
Adorable, angry
Lean, lucky.

Friend acrostic

Learning Objective: To write an acrostic poem based on the word 'friend'.

Name _____ **Date** _____

Write a poem about your friend. Begin each line with the letters of F R I E N D. End the poem with a line of your own.

F _____

R _____

I _____

E _____

N _____

D _____

_____

Learning Objective: To create a group shape poem.

Name _____ **Date** _____

Cut out words and phrases from newspapers, magazines and comics. As a group, stick the cut-out words inside the shape.

Sounds peculiar

Learning Objective: To write phrases or sentences with onomatopoeia.

Name _____ **Date** _____

Read the words on the page. Use each word in a phrase or sentence. Can you use all the words in a 'sound' poem of your own?

gloopy _____

_____

pring _____

_____

slurping _____

_____

squishy _____

_____

CRACKLE _____

_____

boing _____

_____

NON-FICTION

Most writing in the real world combines several text types. However, separating out the 'pure' text types and structures, explicitly naming their individual features can help students gain a better understanding. Explain and use these features and encourage boys to use them in their own writing.

★ Share books which appeal to boys and provide opportunities to respond to them – role-play, dramatisation etc.

★ Share books which appeal to boys and provide opportunities to respond to them, using a range of media, including electronic.

★ Create a bank of relevant vocabulary, phrases and prompts which help thinking, planning and reviewing.

★ Use *Talk for writing* principles and provide lots of opportunity to talk and collaborate prior to and throughout the writing process.

★ Display, demonstrate and discuss model texts and visuals and give a clear purpose for each task.

★ Ensure children discuss and agree text purpose and audience.

★ Provide questions for planning and a range of 'frames' for use.

★ Make available a range of tools, including ICT tools.

★ Display work in progress and finished work, in different versions.

★ Ensure opportunities for review and reflection are available and provide effective feedback.

LABELS, CAPTIONS & LISTS

Purpose	(labels & captions)	to add information to a diagram, photograph or illustration
	(lists)	to inform about a number of items or tasks
Structure	(labels)	text which names and gives information about a diagram or picture, usually with a leader line
	(captions)	a phrase or sentence that adds information to a diagram or picture
	(lists)	on a series of lines, may have a heading
Language features	(labels)	a single word or short phrase including nouns and/or adjectives
	(captions)	a phrase or sentence with present tense verbs
	(lists)	items often separated by commas; verbs may be imperative tense
Visual features	(labels)	leader lines to text
	(captions)	adjacent to image or diagram
	(lists)	usually written vertically

Cross-curricular suggestions

Science and technology
★ Children add labels and captions to diagrams from texts and to own diagrams.

Geography
★ Children add labels to maps of local area and to those accompanying subject topics.

Art
★ Ask children to draw and label the food they ate at lunch.

Teacher's notes

Use the **Challenge Cards** (Resource Sheet 35) to extend the unit.

Activity Sheet 1

Display Resource Sheet 30 and discuss the labels, captions and lists with the children; ask them to find examples of each from the classroom library. Display the activity sheet for the class. Ask the children to find the list on the page and then encourage them to find the items from the list on the map. Give the children copies of the activity sheet in pairs and ask them to label the map using the words from the list.

Activity Sheet 2

In this activity, the children read captions, and choose which one goes with which picture and write the caption below the picture. Together, identify captions from books then give the activity to children individually, or in pairs, to complete.

Activity Sheet 3

In this activity, the children cut out the labels and stick them on the diagram of a bike. For some children, you might like to mask the labels before copying the sheet and ask the children to write the labels using their own knowledge rather than sticking the words in place. Resource Sheets 31 and 32 have alternative illustrations for labelling.

Activity Sheet 4

Discuss with the children what they would need to take with them for a weekend camping – talk about everything they would do and what they would need for each activity. In pairs, ask them to discuss the weekend activities and to make a list of the things they will need to take with them using the activity sheet. Resource Sheet 33 focuses on planning a party and can be used to extend the work on lists.

Activity Sheet 5

Display a large photograph or diagram of an animal or insect and ask children to describe the animal parts. If time permits, give them time to discuss with a partner, before asking for their ideas. Ask them to name body parts with correct names when possible. Write the words on labels and ask children to stick them onto the picture. Repeat the activity (with a different animal), but encourage the boys to use sentences as captions for the body parts. Give copies of the activity sheet to pairs and ask them to do the same with the two animals shown.

REFLECTION & FEEDBACK suggestions

Ask the children to say how labels are different from captions and to write definitions for display. Ask children to display diagrams without labels and captions, beside diagrams with labels and captions. Then talk about how useful labels and captions are.

Getting Started

What's on my table?

Encourage the children to write what's on their table, as a list of items. Compare their list with other children in the class and the teacher.

Label or caption

Play a game where you read a label or a caption from around the classroom. Challenge children to be the first to locate it and say whether it is a label or a caption.

What does it say?

Ask the children to write a caption about their friend or partner on a sticky note. Each places their caption on their partner's forehead without letting them read it. Partners have to guess what the caption says by asking yes/no questions.

Caption the photos

Invite the children to perform a variety of actions in small groups, such as touching toes, hopping etc. Take digital photos of the actions. Display the photos and invite the children to write captions for the photos.

Category lists

Write three headings on the whiteboard: Toys, Kitchen, Zoo. Ask children to name as many items as possible belonging to each category. In pairs, ask children to give a category to their partner and see how many nouns he can think of, then swap roles.

Activity Sheet 1
Label a map

Learning Objective: To use words from a list to add labels.

Name _____ **Date** _____

Read the list of words at the bottom of the map. Find where they are on the map and write labels to show them. One has been done to help you.

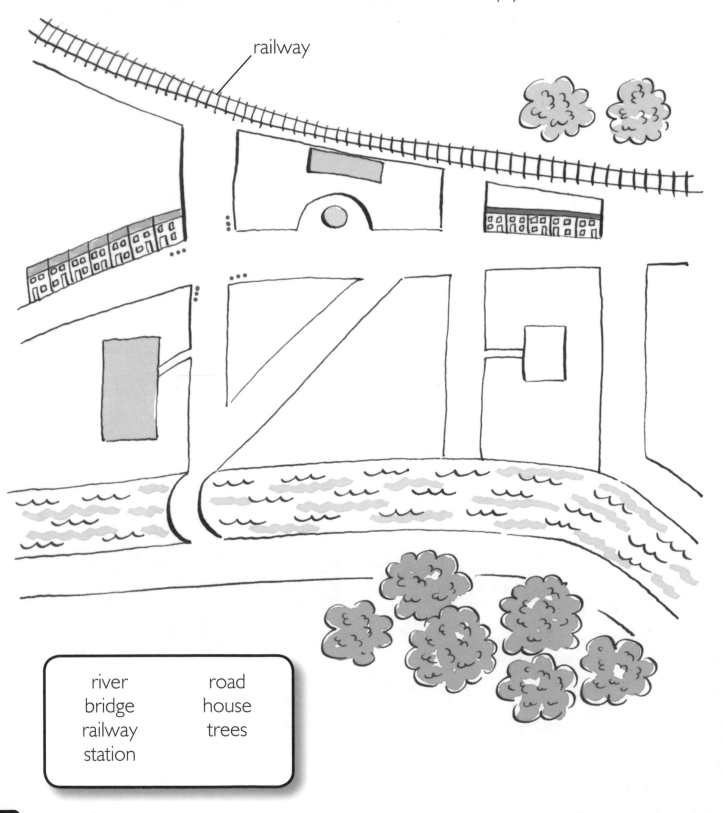

river	road
bridge	house
railway	trees
station	

LABELS, CAPTIONS & LISTS
Brilliant Ideas to Get Boys Writing 5–7 © A & C Black

Activity Sheet 2
Which caption?

Learning Objective: To select appropriate captions and write them.

Name _____ **Date** _____

Which caption goes with which hobby? Write the caption you think matches each picture in the space underneath.

Captions:

Jim scores the winning goal.

Judo keeps you fit and healthy.

A scooter is a great way to get around.

Sky diving is exciting.

_____   _____

_____   _____

Label the bike

Learning Objective: To add labels to a diagram.

Name _____ **Date** _____

Cut out the labels. Stick them onto the diagram in the correct spaces. Can you add any more labels?

labels:

| wheel | saddle | handle bar | gears | chain | tyre | spokes |

Let's go camping

Learning Objective: To write a list.

Name _____ **Date** _____

What would you need to take with you for a weekend camping trip? Write a list.

List

Learning Objective: To describe body features of an animal and insect.

Name _____ Date _____

Name each animal (or insect).
Name the body parts.
Describe its colour, feel and sound.
Describe how it moves.

name

_____
_____
_____
_____
_____
_____
_____
_____
_____

name

_____
_____
_____
_____
_____
_____
_____
_____
_____

DESCRIPTION

Purpose	to give details of an object or a concept
Structure	headings, sentences that give specific detail
Language features	present tense; adjectives of size, colour, comparison; specific nouns
Visual features	often accompanied by an illustration or photograph
Examples	caption on drawing or photo; label on model; email about event

Cross-curricular suggestions

Nature study
★ Take children outside and ask them to describe something they see to a partner. The partner has to guess what was described and point to it. Then swap roles.

Social Science
★ Use photographs of the school or local environment, historical buildings, motorways, shopping centres, etc. Ask children to discuss in a group what they can see. Ask them to write three descriptive sentences about their photograph to share with the class. Make a wall display and label all the buildings.

Teacher's notes

Use the **Challenge Cards** (Resource Sheet 39) to extend the unit.

Activity Sheet 1

Take a photograph of each child and stick on to the activity sheet. Ask children to describe each part of their face – their hair, smile, the way they are looking at the camera – to a partner and then write a description on the sheet, using the prompts. Mix up the activity sheets. Ask children to pick one that is not their own, read the description out loud and ask the others to guess whose sheet it is. Display the sheets.

Activity Sheet 2

Display Resource Sheet 36 and discuss the model text. Show an everyday object, e.g. a lunch box or some clothing. Encourage the children to talk about what it is called, what shape it is, what it is made from, how it is used, etc. Work with them to create a description using three or four sentences. Give the activity sheet to pairs of children. If possible show some of the objects, as this may help some children. Ask the pairs to discuss each item using the words in the box, then choose one item and write a description. Use Resource Sheet 37 to extend the work.

Activity Sheet 3

Read examples of descriptions of places/settings in fiction, then discuss how these descriptions are different from factual descriptions. Explain that in stories, descriptions are usually written in the past tense, but a factual description of a place often uses the present tense. Ask the children to look out of the window and describe what they can see. Encourage them to use factual adjectives e.g. 'there are three trees; the sky is blue; there are three small clouds' and so on. Ask them to look at the picture on the activity sheet and to write three sentences to describe the scene using the present tense.

Activity Sheet 4

Ask children when they think it might be important to observe things closely and be able to give a detailed, accurate description. Examples might include: witnessing a crime or an accident; telling someone about a special place; describing something from a science activity. Ask them to suggest why it's important that a factual description is accurate. Give the activity sheet to pairs of children. Hide the questions and ask them to look closely at the picture together and discuss what they see. Cover the picture and ask them to answer the questions, before revealing the picture again. How accurate were their descriptions? Resource Sheet 38 gives further opportunity to extend work on looking for accurate detail.

Activity Sheet 5

During a shared session, read descriptions of animals from report texts, without naming the animal or showing illustrations. Can children guess the animal being described? Discuss the use of language – present tense verbs, factual adjectives of colour, size, shape and number. Display an enlarged copy of the activity sheet and create a short description of the picture together. Ask the children to write their own description of the animal on their sheet.

REFLECTION & FEEDBACK suggestions

Discuss the importance of using your senses when describing items. Display a large image of an object or scene. Focus on the use of senses when asking children to provide words to describe the object or the scene.

GETTING STARTED

Building a vocabulary

Brainstorm descriptive words from the immediate environment. Create a fast game of listing 10 words in activity breaks. Give children a stimulus, e.g. Look out of the window, what do you see? Look at your feet on the ground, what do you see? Prompt them for colour, size, texture, smell, sound, etc. Make class lists and add to them.

Reading pictures

Provide strips of paper for children to make notes while 'reading pictures' in non-fiction books. Ask them to list features and the special vocabulary that they find. Ask them to leave the strip in the book for other children to find what has been listed and to add to

Talking before writing

Allow time to share descriptions of what children actually see. Emphasise looking at the evidence in photographs, models or objects. Draw their attention to the whole and the parts. Ask them to use descriptive phrases. Model standard linguistic forms back to them. Encourage them to add further details.

Barrier games

Play a barrier game where two children sit back to back. One child has a tray of different objects. The child picks an object and describes it in as much detail as possible without naming the object. The other child guesses what the object is or attempts to draw the object as it is being described.

Descriptive response

Provide a collection of pictures of everyday items on cards in a container. One child selects a card and describes one aspect of the object. The next child adds a word or phrase to describe another aspect, but repeats the example from the previous child. A third child adds further. Some children will benefit from holding a real object; others can be encouraged to use descriptive phrases and sentences. Write descriptive/ words and phrases and/or sentences on a whiteboard.

I feel, I think

Using a 'secret bag', place an object inside for children to feel and describe. Use prompts such as shape, parts, surface, etc. to help them use a wide range of words. One partner feels the object inside, the other records what they describe. After three or four features are described, reveal the object and use its name to create a heading. Swap and discuss.

I am special

Learning Objective: To describe own features from photograph.

Name _____ **Date** _____

I am ....

I have a ....

My eyes are ....

My head has ....

I smile like ....

Describe it

Learning Objective: To describe attributes of everyday objects.

Name _____ Date _____

Choose words from the word box to describe each of these objects.
Choose one object and write three sentences to describe it.

Word box

paper   plastic   square

sides   round   cover

front   back   straps

handles   top   bottom

wood   coloured   drink

food   games   throw

writing   drawing

playing   carrying   eating

drinking   reading

Description of _____

_____

_____

_____

_____

_____

Through the window

Learning Objective: To write sentences in the present tense to give a factual description.

Name _____ **Date** _____

What can you see out of this window? Write three (or more) sentences to describe the scene.

_____

_____

_____

_____

_____

Remember!
Use present tense verbs such as 'it is' and 'they are'. Use colour words, size words and number words to describe things.

Be a witness!

Learning Objective: To observe a scene and then write an accurate description.

Name _____ **Date** _____

Hide the questions at the bottom of the sheet. Look closely at the picture. Talk with your partner about what is happening and what details you can see. Now cover the picture and answer the questions. Then uncover the picture and check how many details you remembered.

fold here

- -

Questions:

1: How many people are in the picture?

2: How many men are in the picture?

3: How many women are in the picture?

4: Name two things the man is wearing and describe them.

5: Did the dog lift its leg at the lamp post?

6: Where was the lamp post?

7: What was in the shop window?

8: What sort of car did you see?

9: What was the woman wearing?

Activity Sheet 5
Tiger description

Learning Objective: To write a paragraph that describes an animal, using factual adjectives.

Name _____ Date _____

Look carefully at the picture of a tiger. Write sentences in a paragraph to describe it. Think about these questions: How many? What shape? What size? What colour?

_____

_____

_____

_____

_____

INSTRUCTIONS

Purpose	to describe how to do or make something or to direct someone
Structure	heading to state goal; list of items needed; sequence or steps in order; statement of outcome
Language features	sentences beginning with verbs, often action verbs; present tense; time conjunctions; descriptive phrases
Visual features	bullet points or numbered steps; illustrated steps and picture of finished product to support text
Examples	recipe; directions; instructions for making items and playing games

Cross-curricular suggestions

Design & Technology
★ Provide materials and instructions for making a simple phone. Ask pairs of children to follow the instructions and make the phone. The first instruction needs to say read ALL of the instructions first!

PHSE
★ Teach children a new ball game such as 'Tunnel Ball'. Later ask them to describe each step in the game so that they can teach others.

English
★ Discuss words that give a time order, such as first, second, etc. Expand childrens' use of these words to include more general words such as before, then, after and first, next, last. Talk about the reasons writers use such words in procedural texts.

Teacher's notes

Use the **Challenge Cards** (Resource Sheet 44) to extend the unit.

Activity Sheet 1

Display Resource Sheet 40 and discuss the structure of writing a set of instructions. Show photographs of funny faces (Resource Sheet 41) made from food, such as bread slices, cup cakes or biscuits. Talk about the food ingredients and the equipment needed to make the funny faces. Provide ingredients and ask children to make their own faces using bread and a mixture of edible ingredients to create eyes, hair, etc. When they have finished, give them the activity sheet and ask them to write down their ingredients and the steps they took to make their face. Less able children may provide spoken text for a scribe. Finally, they eat their creation.

Activity Sheet 2

Display Resource Sheet 42 and discuss various routes with the children. Model instructional language as they walk, stop, turn etc. For example, 'Come out of the school gates turn right, walk to the corner and turn right again. Cross the road. Who lives here?' Make a list of useful words for the children to use when they are giving or writing instructions. Ask children to give instructions for others to follow and say where they are. Give the activity sheet to pairs of children and ask them to look at the map, trace the journey to Peter's house and write the instructions. If some pairs finish early, ask them if there is an alternative route.

Activity Sheet 3

Show children a pattern of beads threaded on a string. Talk about the selection of each bead in order. For example, 'start with a round red bead, add a yellow square one then a blue flat one and finally a pink one. Then start again.' Ask children to give oral instructions for several bead patterns. Encourage the use of order words and also descriptive words to identify different beads. Give children the activity sheet and ask them to draw three patterns for building blocks and give the instructions for the pattern they like best.

Activity Sheet 4

Display the two sets of instructions on Resource Sheet 43. Read both sets of instructions and discuss which set is the most effective and why. Collaborate with the children to cross out any unnecessary words and re-write set A. Provide the children with copies of the activity sheet and ask them to work with a partner, read the instructions and, together, work out what can be omitted. Then ask them to re-write the instructions.

Activity Sheet 5

Tell children that they are going to write the instructions to accompany a set of diagrams for making a kite. Ask them to think about the action word they need for each part of the task. Brainstorm a list of action words on the whiteboard as a reference. Give the activity sheet to pairs of children.

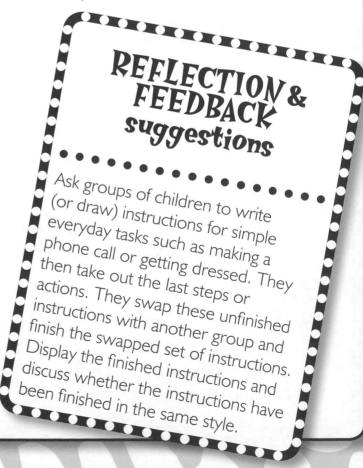

REFLECTION & FEEDBACK suggestions

Ask groups of children to write (or draw) instructions for simple everyday tasks such as making a phone call or getting dressed. They then take out the last steps or actions. They swap these unfinished instructions with another group and finish the swapped set of instructions. Display the finished instructions and discuss whether the instructions have been finished in the same style.

GETTING STARTED

School day actions

Take a series of photographs of the class in action during the day. Write instructions that start with a verb, for example, 'walk in the hallway, sit quietly on the mat, hold your pencil correctly'. Suggest children use WordArt on the computer to make the instructions.

Reading instructions

Offer children several models of instructions from a range of curriculum areas. Working with a small group, ask them to talk about ways they are the same and ways they are different. For example, are they lists, numbered sentences or oral instructions?

Getting around

Draw a map of the classroom on the whiteboard. In groups, ask children to set each other tasks to get from place to place in the classroom using instructions, e.g. from your desk to the teacher's desk. As one child says the instructions, they can be recorded verbally or in writing. After everyone has had a turn, check the instructions. This could also be done with a map of the school.

Lists again

Ask children to select a task topic and to list all of the things that are needed to complete the task. Suggest making a puppet, playing a game, getting ready for school, building a model etc.

Watch and re-tell

Play a miming game where children perform a specific procedure and the others guess what procedure is being performing. Record the performances and ask children to write a set of instructions for others to repeat the procedure. Discuss the use of appropriate verbs in the instructions.

Barrier games

Pairs of children sit back to back. One draws a picture then gives the other child instructions to draw the same thing. Another version is to have one child record the instructions. Play them to a group to see if the children can reproduce a similar drawing by following the instructions on the recording.

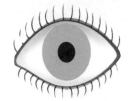 

Funny faces

Learning Objective: To write a set of instructions from experience.

Name _____ **Date** _____

First list what you need to make your face. Then write instructions to tell someone how to make a funny face. Draw what it looked like.

Title:
You will need:

Instructions:

1.	
2.	
3.	
4.	

INSTRUCTIONS
Brilliant Ideas to Get Boys Writing 5–7 © A & C Black

Going to Peter's house

Learning Objective: To write instructions in correct sequence.

Name _____ Date _____

Look at the map and draw how to get to Peter's house. Write the instructions.

To Peter's house

INSTRUCTIONS **97**

Activity Sheet 3
Build it up

Learning Objective: To write detailed and specific instructions.

Name _____ **Date** _____

Draw two different block patterns to make a tower from coloured blocks. Use four blocks only and then repeat the pattern. Write the instructions for each pattern underneath.

example:

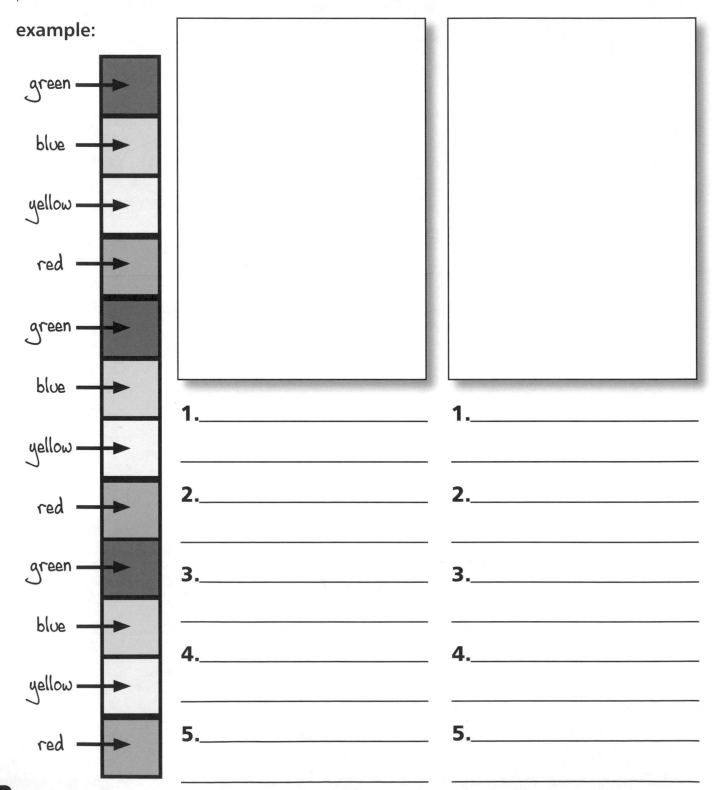

green

blue

yellow

red

green

blue

yellow

red

green

blue

yellow

red

1._____   1._____

_____   _____

2._____   2._____

_____   _____

3._____   3._____

_____   _____

4._____   4._____

_____   _____

5._____   5._____

_____   _____

Too many words

Learning Objective: To improve a set of instructions.

Name _____ **Date** _____

Which words can you cross out or put in a different order?
Re-write the instructions so they are easy to follow.

This tells you how to make a robot

You need all these things to make a robot:
One large cereal box that is empty
Four cardboard tubes
One small box
Glue
Silver paint
Black paint
Paint brushes
Any other things to decorate it

You can glue each tube onto the large cereal box to make two arms and two legs.

Then you should glue the smaller box on the top to make the head.

Paint the robot with silver paint.

If you want to, decorate the robot with wool for hair or buttons for switches.

Use black paint for the face.

Now you can play with your robot.

Activity Sheet 5
Making a kite

Learning Objective: To write instructions from diagrams.

Name _____ Date _____

Look at each diagram for making a kite Write the instruction for each step. Start each sentence with an action word.

You will need:

1._____

_____

2._____

_____

3._____

_____

4._____

_____

INSTRUCTIONS
Brilliant Ideas to Get Boys Writing 5–7 © A & C Black

RECOUNTS

Purpose	to describe an event or series of events in a factual way
Structure	opening followed by paragraphs covering where, when, who and what and a closing statement
Language features	past tense verbs; time connectives
Visual features	photographs; illustrations; diagrams; maps and timelines
Examples	letters, diaries, news telling, newspapers, biography, autobiography

Cross-curricular suggestions

PSHE
★ After a visit to the school by a community person, ask children to make some notes to be used for an oral or written recount.

Geography
★ To support a recount of a class visit to a museum or a historical site, ask children to draw a map of the path they took through the exhibit. A map of the site may be available as a model.

Science
★ Record the growth of some new plants at school over a period of time. Ask children to write a recount of the experiment over the period using the scientific information they have recorded.

Teacher's notes

Use the **Challenge Cards** (Resource Sheet 51) to extend the unit.

Activity Sheet 1

Use Resource Sheet 46 to prompt oral recounts of children's weekend activities. Display the words, removing each one as it is used until none are left. Give children the activity sheet to discuss and then make notes about a school or family event, using the prompts. Children cut their sheet up and use the cards for an oral recount to the class.

Activity Sheet 2

Read a range of recounts to children and explore the information given in the first sentence, or display the introduction on Resource Sheet 47. The introduction usually frames the recount, telling *when, where and who*. The detail of *what happens* is in later sentences. Ask children to write the first sentence for three different recounts suggested by illustrations on the activity sheet.

Activity Sheet 3

Discuss a recent event. Use the *who, where, when* and *what* prompts to help with sequence. Ask the children to describe how they felt. Together, rehearse writing some sentences about feelings. Provide the activity sheet and ask them to draw and write details in each section. Then, cut out the sections and re-order them with a partner to work out the best sequence for their recount.

Activity Sheet 4

Take photographs throughout a school day for a recount. Display the activity sheet and answer the *who, where, when* questions together and write an introductory sentence on a sheet of paper. Give groups five or six photos and ask them to put them in order, writing one sentence for each photo on their sheet. These can be cut out and pasted under each photograph for a giant recount. Then write a comment about the day together.

Activity Sheet 5

Display and discuss the model on Resource Sheet 47. Ask the children to talk to a partner about a recent trip. Give the activity sheet (copied to A3) to pairs of children to make notes – text or drawing. These questions help set the 'introduction' of the recount. Encourage children to record as many 'episodes' as they can remember in 'What happened'. In a plenary, discuss their responses and ask some to read aloud.

Activity Sheet 6

Recap on the 'episodes' from the previous activity. Make a class list of 'linking' words. Ask children to record events for their recount – text or drawing on the sheet. Resource Sheets 48 and 49 provide differentiated frames. Encourage children to add a 'personal comment' at the end of the report.

Activity Sheet 7

Ask children to take photos or make notes about a family visit. Give each child the activity sheet and ask them to talk to their partner about the events of the visit, to refresh their memory and then write about each, alternating talk with writing. Discuss the time order words on the sheet. Are there alternatives?

Activity Sheet 8

Prior to a local community member visit, ask children to write the questions they want answered on the activity sheet. Discuss ways to record the information - listening for answers, note making, audio recording - and agree how to record information from the visitor. After reviewing the answers to their questions, display Resource Sheet 50 and jointly write a recount.

Activity Sheet 9

Talk about the importance of *not* writing every detail. Discuss the difference between big ideas and important detail against everyday information that is not needed. Ask the children, in pairs, to plan and write a recount about school sports day. Use the activity sheet for notes and Resource Sheet 50 to organise the recount if necessary. Ask children to write a finished version or type it on the computer.

REFLECTION & FEEDBACK suggestions

Review the recounts and ask the children to choose the one they think gives the best account of an event, discuss their reasons. Summarise orally the five most important things to include in a recount.

GETTING STARTED

Making notes

Use discussion to explore the details and sequence of information by collaborating to write some notes, to help later. Review any information collected during a trip to add more detail to the notes.

Time smart

Brainstorm words that show and order time. Start with morning, afternoon, evening and extend to connecting words such as firstly, next and lastly. Keep these for children to refer to when writing.

Audience

Talk about how to appeal to different audiences. Compare the different needs of parents, classmates and school visitors. Role-play a recount for two different audiences.

Questions

Use headings such as When, Where, Who, What, How to brainstorm questions about events. Write the questions on charts for display. Encourage children to ask these questions when responding to each other's oral or written recounts.

Taking photos

Encourage two or three children to take photos of class events so that many perspectives are available. Display them as a timeline of the event with captions.

Collecting visual information

Brochures and maps can be collected freely, community organisations may provide them. Use the internet to gather other information too. Engage children in talk and note making as they read and view these.

Note making

Learning Objective: To structure an oral recount of a past event.

Name _____ **Date** _____

Write what you want to say in each box.
Cut along the lines and hold these notes as you talk. They will help you remember what you want to say.

Who

When

Where

What

How

RECOUNTS
Brilliant Ideas to Get Boys Writing 5–7 © A & C Black

The first sentence

Learning Objective: To write introductory sentences using important information for a recount.

Name _____ **Date** _____

Look at the pictures of these events. Where and when did this happen? Who was involved? Write the first sentence for each event.

_____

_____

_____

_____

_____

_____

_____

_____

_____

_____

_____

_____

_____

_____

Activity Sheet 3
How did I feel?

Learning Objective: To add feelings to a recount and work out the best sequence.

Name _____ **Date** _____

Draw what happened in each section. Write a sentence for each one. Cut out the sections and re-order them into the best order.

Who?	**What?**

When?	**Where?**

How I felt?

Activity Sheet 4
Group writing

Learning Objective: To use photographs as stimulus for writing about an event.

Name _____ **Date** _____

Look at the photographs and write a sentence about each photo. Write a personal comment about the day.

| Who | Where | When |

1st	
2nd	
3rd	
4th	
5th (depending on photos)	
Last	
Personal Comment	

Brilliant Ideas to Get Boys Writing 5–7 © A & C Black

Our trip notes

Learning Objective: To write or draw notes after a class trip.

Name _____ **Date** _____

Talk to your partner about your class trip. Answer the questions in the boxes.

Where did you go on the trip?

Who went on the trip?

When did you go?

How did you get there?

How long did it take?

What was the weather like?

What happened?

Our trip

Learning Objective: To write or draw a short report on a class trip.

Name _____ **Date** _____

Draw or write the events from your trip in the boxes. Write good link words in the circles. Don't forget a personal comment.

1.

4.

2.

3.

Personal comment

Brilliant Ideas to Get Boys Writing 5–7 © A & C Black

Timeline

Learning Objective: To sequence events for writing and use time connectives.

Name _____ **Date** _____

Talk about your weekend with a partner. Talk then write about each part.

Who   **Where**   **When**

| First |
| Then |
| Next |
| After that |
| Lastly |
| Personal Comment |

Our visitor

Learning Objective: To record spoken information for writing.

Name _____ **Date** _____

What information do you want
to know from the visitor? Write
a question under each heading.

Who

When

Where

What

How

Sports day

Learning Objective: To identify the important ideas and details to include in a recount for parents.

Name _____ **Date** _____

Many things happen at the school sports day. Decide what is most important for parents to read about.
Make notes about all the details you need to include.

Who participated in the day?

Where was it held?

When was it? **What** was the weather like?

What happened?

What did you think?

INFORMATION TEXTS

Purpose	to give factual information about a topic
Structure	information organised by topic area, often non-chronological
Language features	may have chapters or sections; headings and subheadings; contents page; index; glossary; labels and captions
Visual features	photographs, illustrations and diagrams
Examples	books on other curriculum areas such as geography, science or art; encyclopaedia and dictionaries

Cross-curricular suggestions

Science/Geography
★ Children use the contents pages and indexes to find information. Children scan a page to locate information by key word, headings and sub-headings.

Science
★ Ask children to draw a diagram of a living thing. They swap illustrations with a partner and label each other's diagram.

PSHE
★ Review information texts dealing with the care of an animal. Use this as a model to create a group text about the care of a different animal.

Use the **Challenge Cards** (Resource Sheet 55) to extend the unit.

Activity Sheet 1

Talk together about how we choose a book. Discuss the features on the covers that help in the choice – title, author, back cover blurb. Provide pairs with the activity sheet and ask them to read and then label the 'fiction' or 'non-fiction' examples by writing F or NF in the spaces.

Activity Sheet 2

Using non-chronological reports with contents and index pages, ask the children to predict the information they contain. Ask them to think of something they could find out about in each book. Model how to find the information using a contents page and/or an index. Provide the activity sheet and ask the children to label the pages and answer the questions.

Activity Sheet 3

Explain that you are going to write a class book about bikes. Discuss and list what the children already know. Can they suggest other information for the book? Where could they find it? Provide the activity sheet and ask pairs to complete the first three columns. Allow sufficient time for research using the library or the internet before they complete the chart.

Activity Sheet 4

Together explore paragraphs, headings and sub-headings in an information text. Talk about the information on the KWWL charts and how it could be grouped for the class book. Model adding key words and phrases to an enlarged copy of the activity sheet. Children work with a partner to create their own spidergrams.

REFLECTION & FEEDBACK suggestions

Read the class book about bikes to the children. Discuss what worked well and what could be improved. Ask the children to say how an alphabetically ordered information book differs from other information texts.

Activity Sheet 5

In a shared session look at what's in an information text introduction, usually general facts about the class of things (i.e. bikes). Discuss what children think should be in the class book introduction. Ensure they don't add too much detail which might be repeated in the text. Give pairs the activity sheet and ask them to list key words or phrases for a contents list and to draft a short paragraph for an introduction, then compare with another pair. Can they improve their work? Compile a class contents list with enough 'chapters' for each group to have at least one.

Activity Sheet 6

Display Resource Sheet 46 and discuss the 'chapter' model. Provide each group with a 'chapter' from the contents list and the activity sheet. Invite them to write a first draft for a chapter in the class book.

Activity Sheet 7

Look at the different types of illustration in information texts – photographs, diagrams with labels, cross-sections, maps etc. How will groups illustrate their 'chapter' – digital photos, find illustrations or draw their own? Give the activity sheet to groups and ask them to write their second draft and add illustrations.

Activity Sheet 8

Display Resource Sheet 54 and explore how information is organised in alphabetically ordered texts such as encyclopaedia. How would the bike text be organised if it were written in this format? Discuss the use of language and then ask the children to work with a partner and write information for at least two of the headwords on the activity sheet.

Activity Sheet 9

Explore websites about bikes with the children: *www.bikeability.org.uk*; *www.bsca.org.uk*; *www.mikeandthebike.com*; *www.ba-gb.com* and *www.childrensmountainbikes.co.uk*. Discuss the way in which the information is organised. How different are these from texts about bikes? Invite the children to design a webpage about bikes using their research. They can use the sheet to help them organise their ideas.

Getting Started

Group facts

Give a group a topic to think about that is relevant to work they are doing in another area of the curriculum. Ask them to talk about what they know about the topic. Encourage them to group their information into short sections, e.g. appearance, uses, habitat and so on. Ask the members to take a section each and present their information orally as a group talk.

Fiction or non-fiction?

Provide a variety of books about sport including both non-fiction books and stories. Give the children post-it notes and ask them to label the books either 'fiction' or 'non-fiction'.

Dictionary race

Play a Dictionary race game once a day. Give a word to the children and challenge them to find it in a dictionary using their alphabet knowledge. Time them and write the time up as a target to beat.

What's inside?

Provide the children with an information text. Read the title and the back cover blurb. Brainstorm a list of questions that the children think might be answered by the text.

Encyclopedia order

Prepare some word cards that are relevant to a topic the children are familiar with from another curriculum area. Give small groups a selection of the cards and ask them to pick a card each, then organise themselves as a group of human 'head words' for an encyclopaedia on the topic.

Activity Sheet 1
What sort of book is it?

Learning Objective: To distinguish between story books and information texts.

Name _____ **Date** _____

Which of these are from a story (fiction) and which are from an information book (non-fiction)? Write F for fiction or NF for non-fiction in the space beside each example.

Cars, Trucks & Lorries

The Mystery on The Midnight Train

Jonny Dymond AND THE MISSING RUBY
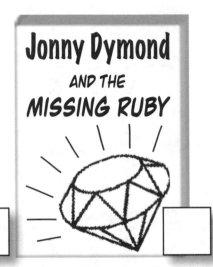

How to Grow BEANS

The Ugly Duckling

All you ever wanted to know about SPIDERS

★Can Daniel solve the mystery?
★Will he be able to save his best friend?
★This thrilling new story takes Daniel into strange and mysterious places!

How does a Weaver Bird build its nest? Where does an Albatross sleep? Which is it – an Eagle or a Hawk? These are just some of the fascinating facts you will find in this A-Z of bird life.

Fe, Fi, Fo, Fum, When Jack heard these sounds he was filled with dread...

Brilliant Ideas to Get Boys Writing 5–7 © A & C Black

Activity Sheet 2
How do I find out?

Learning Objective: To understand the function of contents and index pages.

Name _____ **Date** _____

Which of these lists is a Contents page and which is an index? Write the correct heading at the top of the pages.
Write the page numbers where you can find information to answer the questions.

_____	_____

Which pages tell you about the history of bikes? _____

What things can you read about on page 17? _____

What will you find out about on page 25? _____

In which chapter will you find out about both Mountain bikes and Racing bikes? ____

On which page can you find out about Mountain bike handle bars? _____

On which page will you find out about tyres and wheels? _____

Which list is written in alphabetical order? _____

Activity Sheet 3
Research

Learning Objective: To plan information needed for a class book.

Name _____   Date _____

With your partner, fill in the first three columns of the chart. Research the information and then write what you have learnt in the final column.

K What I already <u>k</u>now	**W** <u>W</u>hat I want to know	**W** <u>W</u>here I might find the information	**L** What I have <u>l</u>earnt

Organising information

Learning Objective: To make notes of key words and phrases; to organise information logically.

Name _____ **Date** _____

Group your information about bikes in topic areas. Add key words and phrases about bikes to the spidergram.

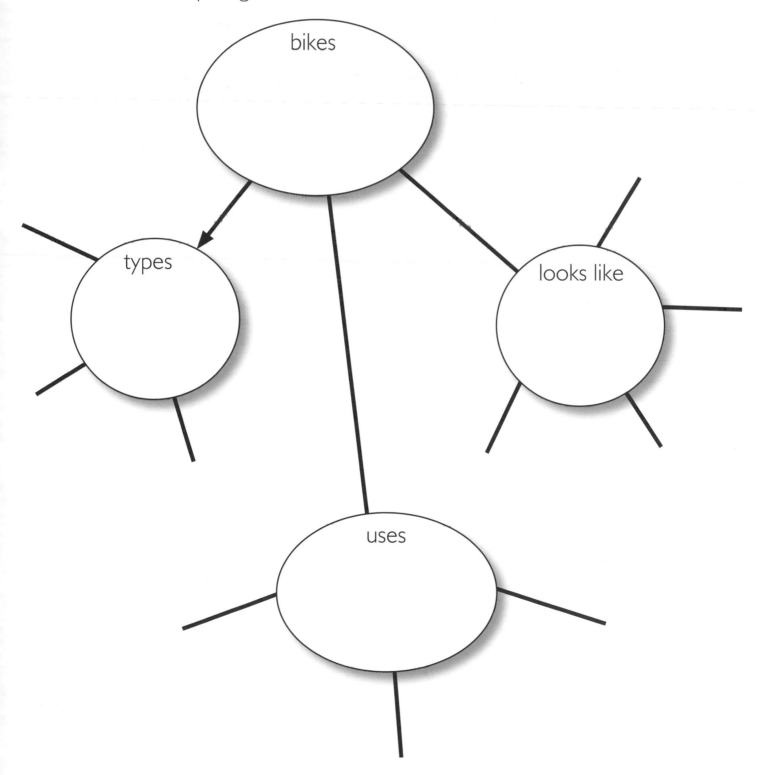

Activity Sheet 5
Contents and introduction

Learning Objective: To write key words to use as a contents list and to write an introductory paragraph.

Name _____ **Date** _____

Write some headings for the contents list in the class book about bikes. Write a draft paragraph to introduce the topic.

OUR BOOK ABOUT BIKES
Contents:
Introduction

who uses them

what they look like

how they work

how they are used

types of bikes

what is the book about

information about the group of items

INFORMATION TEXTS
Brilliant Ideas to Get Boys Writing 5–7 © A & C Black

Planning a first draft

Learning Objective: To plan and write a first draft for a section of a class book.

Name _____ **Date** _____

Work in a group to plan and write a chapter for the class book on bikes.

Chapter heading:
Introductory sentence (for the chapter)
Paragraph text
Closing sentence

Second draft

Learning Objective: To write and illustrate a page for a class book on bikes.

Name _____ **Date** _____

Review the first draft of your chapter and include changes. Write your second draft and add an appropriate illustration with a caption.

Heading and introductory sentence:

Paragraph text:

Illustrations

Caption

Closing sentence:

A-Z of bikes

Learning Objective: To write information for an encyclopaedia.

Name _____ **Date** _____

Fill in the missing information for this A – Z of bikes.

BMX: A small single-speed bike used for racing and doing stunts.

Brakes: _____

_____

_____

Chain: _____

_____

Fork: The part of the frame that holds the front wheel.

Mountain bike: _____

_____

Saddle: _____

_____

Tandem: _____

_____

_____

Wheel: _____

_____

Web page

Learning Objective: To write information for a website page.

Name _____ **Date** _____

Design a web page about bikes using the prompts on the page.

Title:

Write the section headings in the hyperlink shapes

| home page | history | sports | where to ride | stunts | competitions |

eXPLanaTIons

Purpose	to explain a process; how or why something happens or works
Structure	introduction to what is being explained; explanation sequence; closing statement
Language features	present tense, passive verbs, time connectives, cause and effect connectives, technical vocabulary, labels, captions
Visual features	photographs, illustrations and diagrams
Examples	science, technology and history books and electronic articles; radio and television programmes

Cross-curricular suggestions

Science
★ Identify the features of explanation texts in science and ask children to collaborate in drawing or writing an explanation for another class.

Design and technology
★ Children write explanations of how things work that they have made in design and technology.

Art and Design
★ Ask children to explain orally to a classmate how to mix paints to make another colour. Check that the classmate can follow the instructions.

TeaCHeR's notes

Use the **Challenge Cards** (Resource Sheet 62) to extend the unit.

Activity Sheet 1

Ask children to think of explanations they have been given, not instructions (how to do something), but an explanation of how or why something works – an experiment or a game. Provide activity sheet to pairs and ask children to decide upon, and then draw a simple explanation, giving it a title. You could provide a list: how the telephone or digital camera works, how a circuit lights up, how to keep warm or cool, etc. Ensure they talk to their partner and make explicit not just what is happening, but why. Encourage children to write some text, if they are confident. Display and discuss the explanations.

Activity Sheet 2

Display Resource Sheet 58 and talk about what is happening. Focus children on the cause and effect relationship – putting the seed in the soil, giving it food, water and sunshine will make it grow. Encourage them to use conjunctions and time words when giving an explanation about the process. Give pairs the activity sheet and ask them to write an explanation in the boxes. In a plenary, talk about the 'technical' words children used.

Activity Sheet 3

Together read some explanations in non-fiction titles, talk about what is being explained. Display Resource Sheet 59, discuss and highlight the time connectives and cause and effect words. In pairs, give children the activity sheet and ask them to discuss a possible explanation and then to write it in

the boxes. In a plenary, explore some of the explanations, pointing out good use of connective and cause/effect words.

Activity Sheet 4

Look at illustrations which often accompany explanations; sometimes these are cross-sections, to give a better view of the thing being explained. Can the children find examples in books? Discuss where seeds come from. Show children the apple on the activity sheet and ask them to locate the seeds. Give them the activity sheet and ask them, in pairs, to label the parts of the two cross-sections. Make a display of these and other cross-sections.

Activity Sheet 5

Display Resource Sheet 60. Ask the children to look at the life cycle of a butterfly. Encourage them to explain the life cycle sequence. Give out the activity sheets and ask children to make notes on the diagram of the dragon fly life cycle, to help them write an explanation.

Activity Sheet 6

Display and discuss the model text (Resource Sheet 60), focus on the introduction. Explain that they are going to write an explanation about the life cycle of dragonflies. Discuss what they know from the previous activity and scribe some suggested introductions on the board. Provide copies of the activity sheet and ask children to work with a partner to write an introduction, then to use the prompts to plan their explanation. Then ask them to write a polished version in their book or on the computer.

Activity Sheet 7

Discuss the purpose of glossaries. Look together at examples in non-fiction texts and explore the structure, i.e. alphabetical order. Cut out the words on Resource Sheet 61 and give a set to each group. Ask them to organise the words in order as in a glossary. Encourage them to stand in order as a human glossary. Provide children with the activity sheet and dictionaries to look up definitions of the words. Add a glossary to the dragonfly explanations.

REFLECTION & FEEDBACK suggestions

Ask the children which part of the work they completed was the easiest or most enjoyable and why. Talk about how a report text on dragonflies or volcanoes would be similar and how it would be different. Ensure the children are aware that an explanation sequence could feature in a report text.

GETTING STARTED

How does it work?

Provide the children with some mechanical toys, for example, wind-up toys or those that use gravity or pulleys. Encourage the children to give an oral description of what happens when the toy is played with.

And then ...

Encourage the children to develop a range of temporal and causal connectives. Ask them 'what happens when...' for different everyday events, for example, what happens when the school bell rings?

What happens if...?

Give the children building blocks, dominoes, cards or 'jenga' blocks. Encourage them to make constructions and then remove parts from the lower levels to see what happens. Encourage them to explain why the construction collapses using words of time and cause and effect.

Cross sections

Give children a range of fruits, cut in half – do not use apples as these are part of Activity 4. Ask them to draw an illustration of the cross section and then to add labels. Make a display with other cross sections from library books.

Explain what happened

Learning Objective: To draw illustrations to explain what happened.

Name _____ **Date** _____

Draw pictures to explain what happened. Give the explanation a title.

EXPLANATIONS
Brilliant Ideas to Get Boys Writing 5–7 © A & C Black

Flow chart

Learning Objective: To add captions to a flow chart to show the sequence of growth.

Name _____ **Date** _____

Look carefully at the illustrations of the plant. Add an explanation of the sequence to the flow chart.

Activity Sheet 3
Digestive system

Learning Objective: To write simple sentences to add an explanation to a visual.

Name _____ **Date** _____

In the boxes, write an explanation of the digestive system.

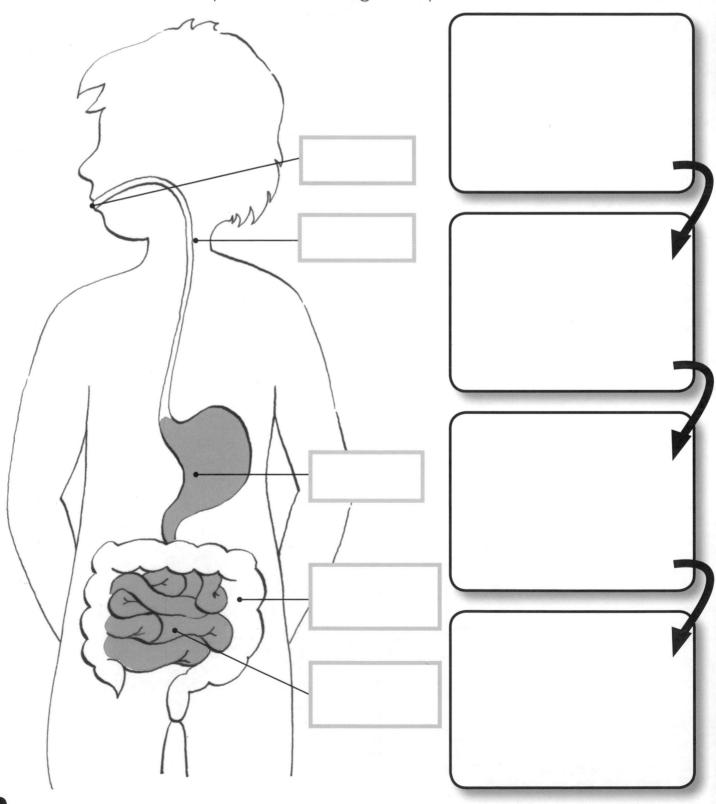

EXPLANATIONS
Brilliant Ideas to Get Boys Writing 5–7 © A & C Black

Cross section

Learning Objective: To add captions to a flow chart to a cross section.

Name _____ **Date** _____

Write labels on the two cross sections.

Learning Objective: To add captions to a flow chart to show the sequence of a life cycle.

Name _____ **Date** _____

Look carefully at this life cycle. Add captions to explain the sequence. Then add an introductory sentence.

Title: The life cycle of a dragon fly

Introduction

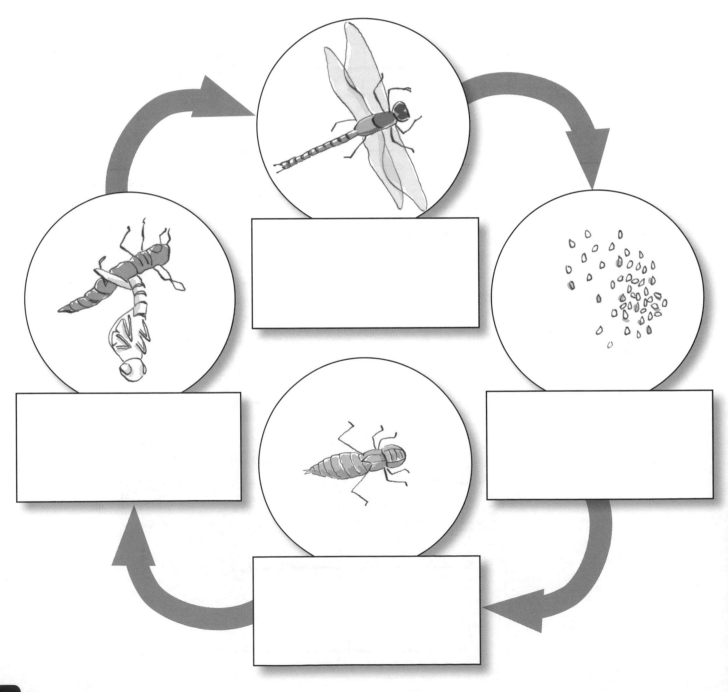

Planning an explanation

Learning Objective: To make notes for a written explanation.

Name _____ Date _____

DRAGON FLIES	
Introduction	
First	
Next	
Then	
Finally	
Closing sentence	
Good words box	Time words: Glossary words:
Cause and effect words	When ... happens, this makes... This results in... If... then... Because.... This causes...

Activity Sheet 7
Glossaries

Learning Objective: To sort words into alphabetical order.

Name _____ **Date** _____

Write the words below in alphabetical order for the glossary. Add a definition for each word.

GLOSSARY
antennae

WORD BOX

insect	larva	pupa	dormant
chrysalis	butterfly	moth	antennae

NON-CHRONOLOGICAL REPORTS

Purpose	to inform using factual information
Structure	introduction, paragraphs ordered by topic; may be written in alphabetical order; may contain an explanation sequence
Language features	present tense verbs; technical terms; descriptions and examples
Visual features	photographs, diagrams and illustrations
Examples	reference books and articles about a class of things (desert animals, lorries, aeroplanes); alphabetically organised texts such as encyclopaedias

Cross-curricular suggestions

Art
★ Children can draw, paint or colour pictures to illustrate their reports.

History
★ Children can compare and report on toys and games from the present with toys and games from the past.

Geography
★ Children can explore games played by children in other parts of the world.

Teacher's notes

Use the **Challenge Cards** (Resource Sheet 66) to extend the unit.

Activity Sheet 1

Explain to the children that they are going to create reports about the games they most enjoy playing. Refer to the list drawn up in 'Getting started'. Provide each child with the activity sheet. Ask them to draw their game and write notes of everything they know about the game using the prompts. Place children in groups and ask them to arrange their sheets in alphabetical order by the name of each game. As their sheet comes up, each child describes their game to the others.

Activity Sheet 2

Discuss the information the children wrote about their favourite games. Explain that when authors write a text about a non-fiction topic they need to make sure the facts they use are accurate, so they do research. Ask the children to work with a partner, talk about and compare the information from Activity 1 and make notes on the activity sheet about what they know already and what else they think they could add to make it more interesting to readers.

Activity Sheet 3

Ask the children to join up with other children who chose the same game and discuss and compare the notes they made in Activity 1. Invite them to use the spidergram on the activity sheet to expand and improve on the information they have, using their researched knowledge and any new details gathered from the discussion.

Activity Sheet 4

Ask the children to return to their original groups. Display the model text on Resource Sheet 63 and identify the language and layout of the non-chronological report. Draw attention to the structure and purpose of the glossary. Invite the children to suggest how they could organise their information about 'Games' using a similar structure. Ask them to brainstorm possible sub-headings for paragraphs and to draw up a list of specific vocabulary. Provide copies of the activity sheet and ask them each to write two paragraphs. Discuss how best to organise their sheets, as pages for the book – alphabetically, or by activity? Collage pages accordingly and number them

Activity Sheet 5

Refer children to the introductory sentences in the model text on Resource Sheet 63. Explain that the paragraphs they have written will be part of a group book about games. Therefore it needs an introduction so that readers will know what information the book will give them. Ask each group to discuss and compare the information in the two paragraphs. Then ask the group to each write three sentences for an introduction about the information.

Activity 6

Ask the children to describe how to find out specific information in a book, e.g. using an index. Together, look at some indexes and ask the children to describe how they are organised. Give pairs the sheet and ask them to find words for the index in a book on games – encourage them to use the library or the internet and to find a word for each letter, including associated words. Then ask groups to prepare an index (and a glossary) for the group book, putting the chosen words in alphabetical order and adding page numbers.

REFLECTION & FEEDBACK suggestions

Give groups one of the writing frames (Resource Sheets 64, 65 and 66) and ask them to make notes for a non-chronological report. Then ask the group to create a report using each heading as a page and adding an index. Ask the groups to read their books to other groups. Discuss the content and layout. How successful are they? Could anything be added or changed to improve them? Display the books for others to read.

GETTING STARTED

Finding out

Take opportunities to model how to find information in texts that are not sequential such as encyclopaedia and other non-chronological reports in other areas of the curriculum.

Long ago games

Discuss the games that the children play. Draw up a list of the most popular games. Ask the children to research popular games played in the past by asking parents and grandparents.

Organise it

Use a shared reading session to draw up a list of the common features of non-chronological reports, such as contents page, index, glossary, present tense verbs, headings and sub-headings, photographs, diagrams, paragraphs.

ABCDEF
Making sense

Provide the children with word cards on different topic areas such as animals or vehicles. Ask them to order them by initial letter and then first two letters. Provide the children with pages from magazines that feature report text, for example nature magazines, hobby magazines. Ask them to cut out the paragraphs and work with a partner to re-order the paragraphs. Talk about how the information is affected by re-ordering.

GHIJKLM

Order!

Play alphabetical order games such as challenging the children to line up alphabetically.

Activity Sheet 1
Favourite games

Learning Objective: To make notes for a non-chronological report.

Name _____ Date _____

Which game do you most enjoy playing?
Draw a picture of it and make notes about it.

I like playing _____

Do you play the game on your own or with others?

What clothes do you wear when you play the game?

Do you need anything special to play the game?

Can you play the game anywhere or is it played in a special place, like a pitch or a hall?

What skills do you need to play?

NON-CHRONOLOGICAL REPORTS

ReSearch

Learning Objective: To use a KWL chart to research information for a non-chronological report.

Name _____

Date _____

Write what you know about your favourite game and what you want to know. Use talk partners, books or the internet to find answers and write what you learned in the last column.

Title:

What I **Know**	What I **Want** to know	What I **Learnt**

NON-CHRONOLOGICAL REPORTS
Brilliant Ideas to Get Boys Writing 5–7 © A & C Black

Game plan

Learning Objective: To write and organise notes for paragraphs for a non-chronological report.

Name _____ **Date** _____

Make notes about your favourite game on the spidergram. Add more arms or circles if you need them.

who plays

where you play

game

skills

rules

Activity Sheet 4
Paragraphs

Learning Objective: To write two paragraphs using present tense verbs and technical vocabulary.

Name _____ **Date** _____

Write two paragraphs about your favourite game using the prompts on the page. Underline any words that will go into a glossary.

TITLE:

Sub-heading:

Who can play?

I enjoy playing...

Where is it played?

This game is played...

Sub-heading:

How do people play?

People can play ...

Special clothes or equipment?

Brilliant Ideas to Get Boys Writing 5–7 © A & C Black

Activity Sheet 5
Introduction

Learning Objective: To write three sentences for an introductory paragraph.

Name _____ Date _____

Write three sentences as an introduction for your group book. Use this model to help you.

GAMES FROM THE PAST

People have always enjoyed playing games. Most games are played in teams or with a partner. Some games are played alone. In this book, you can find out about games that people played in the past.

TITLE:	
Sentence 1 Tell readers general information about the subject.	
Sentence 2 One main thing they can find out about.	
Sentence 3 One other thing they can find out.	

NON-CHRONOLOGICAL REPORTS
Brilliant Ideas to Get Boys Writing 5–7 © A & C Black

Activity Sheet 6
Index

Learning Objective: To write an alphabetically ordered index for a non-chronological report.

Name _____ **Date** _____

Write six index entries for a book about games. Write them on the page in alphabetical order. Use library books to help you.

A B C D E F G

Z

Y

X

W

V

U T S R Q P O N

H

I

J

K

L

M

Index

-
-
-
-
-
-

General reference sheets

These resources can be used as class discussion prompts, by children as part of activities or as classroom display.

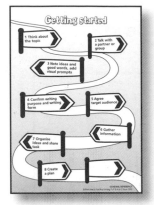

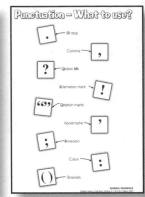

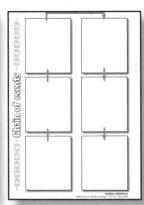

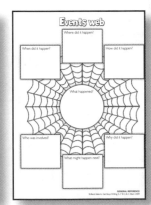

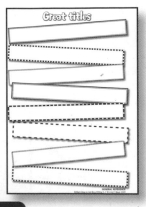

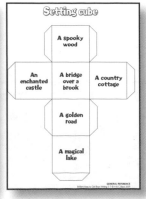

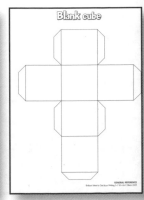